PENGUIN

The Perfect

Furio Monicelli was born in 1924 in Milan. His first novel, *Il gesuita perfetto* (*The Perfect Jesuit*), was published in 1960; it was reissued in 1999 with the title *Lacrime impure* and was the winner of the International Prize. He wrote a second novel, *I giardini segreti* (1961), before taking up a career in journalism, which included a period with the BBC. Until his recent retirement, he taught at the Giuseppe Verdi Conservatory in Milan, where he still lives.

Joseph Farrell teaches Italian at the University of Strathclyde in Glasgow. He has presented several documentaries, and contributes regularly to BBC arts programmes. He has produced versions of plays by Dario Fo and Carlo Toldoni for the stage, and has translated novels by Italian writers including Leonardo Sciascia, Vincenzo Consolo and Daniele Del Giudice. He was awarded the John Florio Prize for the translation of Del Giudice's novel *Take Off*. He is the author of a biography of Dario Fo.

The Perfect Jesuit

FURIO MONICELLI

Translated by Joseph Farrell

PENGUIN BOOKS

PENGUIN BOOKS

Published by the Penguin Group
Penguin Books Ltd, 27 Wrights Lane, London w8 5tz, England
Penguin Putnam Inc., 375 Hudson Street, New York, New York 10014, USA
Penguin Books Australia Ltd, Ringwood, Victoria, Australia
Penguin Books Canada Ltd, 10 Alcorn Avenue, Toronto, Ontario, Canada m4v 3b2
Penguin Books India (P) Ltd, 11 Community Centre, Panchsheel Park,
New Delhi – 110 017, India
Penguin Books (NZ) Ltd, Cnr Rosedale and Airborne Roads,
Albany, Auckland, New Zealand
Penguin Books (South Africa) (Pty) Ltd, 5 Watkins Street,
Denver Ext 4, Johannesburg 2094, South Africa

Penguin Books Ltd, Registered Offices: Harmondsworth, Middlesex, England

First published in 2001

1

Copyright © Furio Monicelli, 1960
Translation copyright © Joseph Farrell, 2001

All rights reserved

The moral right of the translator has been asserted

Set in 11.5/13.5 pt Monotype Dante
Typeset by Rowland Phototypesetting Ltd,
Bury St Edmunds, Suffolk
Printed in England by Clays Ltd, St Ives plc

I

Andrea put all he needed into a suitcase and called for a taxi. He told the driver to take him to Piazza San Giovanni. He bought himself his last packet of cigarettes, then went into the basilica of St John Lateran, where he made his confession and remained a little while in prayer. There was no trace of any emotion in him.

On coming out of the church, he went over to a restaurant on the other side of the square and treated himself to a substantial meal. He thought to himself that back home they must have discovered his flight, but would not be able to pursue him, since he had left no forwarding address. He paid his bill and crossed the square to get on to the bus for Galloro. The day, a drizzly day in late October, was pungent and sad, like remorse. Along the way, through the city's suburbs, across the countryside and towards the glorious Albano Hills, the study of the world seemed to hold a wholly new interest, just when he was on the point of abandoning it. He got off at a little grass-covered square in front of a baroque church attached to a severe grey building. This was the shrine of the Madonna of Galloro, site of the religious novitiate of the Society of Jesus.

He rang at the huge door of the house and, as awkwardly as a new boy on his first day at school, made his way into the entrance hall. The shaven head of a lay-brother appeared from behind the glass door of the booth. Andrea introduced himself, and the other smiled encouragingly. 'We were expecting you,' he said, ushering the young man into a nearby room and asking him to wait there. The room was bare and cold. Andrea sat down on a wooden seat. Two portraits of the Pope hung from the walls. In the oppressive silence, the young man gazed at those enormous, enlarged photographs. Pius XII resembled a character from El Greco, or a portrait by the Great Condé which Andrea had seen somewhere or other. After a few minutes, a tall, robust priest, wearing exactly the expression the occasion required, made his way in.

'I am the novice master,' he said.

Andrea rose to his feet and the superior embraced him. Then he took hold of the postulant's suitcase and led him out of the room. The young man protested and attempted to take back the case but the priest would not let him have it. With that little lesson in humility, he was initiating, there and then, the religious education of the new candidate. Back in the entrance hall, the superior opened a door on which was written the word 'Cloister'. Andrea followed him along a long, neat, dark corridor. He heard the door close behind him with a dull thud.

The first days, still dressed in ordinary clothes, he remained confined in a cell which was not part of the novices' apartment. He scarcely ever saw them. Every evening, he took his meal with the novice master, the tutor of the young men. The master was a courteous man, of extreme simplicity, devout without any trace of exaggeration. Everything in there appeared a marvel to Andrea: the silence, the spiritual practices, the austere atmosphere, serene at certain moments of the day but almost gloomy at others. Having led an unordered life, he lent himself with enthusiasm to the meticulous, iron requirements of the timetable. Every day at the same hour, he carried out the same action, and this seemed to him absurd because he knew that life required infinite transactions and adaptations, and he considered somewhat artificial the scrupulous precision with which every action, even the most trivial, had to be carried out. However, such was the grip of habit that, after a few weeks of the religious life, he experienced a kind of unease inside himself when he did not follow the normal timetable, and that unease, like a taut spring released and settling to the position of rest, only calmed itself when he resumed the common observance.

In the beginning, the state of isolation in which he found himself terrified him. Even if there were many of them in that house, each appeared to live in loneliness. Andrea had done such violence to himself that he felt removed from reality, and that action on himself was so strong and deep that its effects lingered long. Then, quite suddenly, he became aware of everything he had left, and the sacrifice he had made appeared to him in all its immensity, as he had never seen nor felt it when making it. He abandoned himself to prayer, to long periods of meditation, and when he went out for a walk in the vicinity of the house, he found himself so disorientated that it seemed as though the corners of the streets were out of place.

The days rushed by, enclosed in the iron discipline of the timetable. The young man began to make cautious contact with the other brothers, and learned to correct himself, to manoeuvre his way among them, to observe and get to know them in their differences, in their rivalries and solidarity, in their weaknesses and victories. He was happy in their company, and the tumultuous memories of his teenage years now seemed to him a poor thing. He had to struggle continuously against sleep, and this struggle gave him sharpness, lucidity and vivacity of mind. It was as though he was living ten minutes for each minute of the clock, and the number of things he managed to achieve in one day where each instant was dedicated to some activity seemed to him incredible. At night he slept a deep and heavy sleep which nothing could have interrupted.

Andrea was alone in the little bare room on the ground floor which opened on to the huge internal garden. From the window, the panorama stretched out on the one side towards Mount Pardo and on the other towards Ariccia and its valley. In the distance lay the undulating plain, a stage of yellowing vines sloping down towards the green sea of autumn. An iron bed, a prie-dieu facing a brass crucifix, a plain desk, a seat, a white enamel basin and jug made up the furnishing of the room. Andrea rummaged idly in the desk drawers, which were empty, but in a corner he found a holy picture on which these words had been printed in Gothic characters: 'Cursed be he that doeth the work of the Lord deceitfully' (Jeremiah 48: 10).

At that moment, there was a knock at the door, and a lay-brother asked Andrea to go to the father rector's room. The young man climbed the stairs to the first floor and walked along a brightly polished corridor whose walls were bedecked with grand seventeenth-century paintings depicting strange Jesuits of that time in stately, austere poses. There was one, evidently a missionary, who wore on his head an oriental-style turban, and under each portrait, written in oil, were captions summarizing the special talents of the people depicted. One had distinguished himself for wisdom and doctrine, another for the virtue of silence, a third for fearless faith in the midst of heretics and a fourth for unbending firmness of character.

Andrea stopped in front of a door on which was written 'Father Rector', and observed a letterbox, similar to the kind found in post-offices, attached to the wall near the entrance.

He knocked. 'Come in,' said a loud, authoritarian, cordial voice. The novice found himself in a simply furnished room with a more commodious desk than the one in his own room, and behind that desk was seated an elderly man with a drawn face whom Andrea had never seen until that moment. The father rector signalled to him to sit down and sat staring at him in silence for a few seconds.

Andrea lowered his face, formulating inside himself a rash, brazen judgement. He thought that here was the authentic face of ambition, envy and avarice, or else the face of a scheming, moralistic, holier-than-thou man given over to all manner of intrigue and cunning. Immediately afterwards, he felt self-disgust and remorse for having thought such a thing, and was on the point of bursting into tears. When the superior began to speak, Andrea raised his eyes and gradually, as the other continued with his talk, he modified his first impression.

'My son, the novice master has spoken to me favourably about you. We have decided to admit you among us for the trial of the novitiate. Tomorrow there will be the ceremony of your robing and immediately afterwards you can join the other novices, who are keenly awaiting you. Do you realize the nature of the privilege which has been accorded to you in assuming the holy habit of the Society? Blessed are they to whom it is given to understand it . . . For my own part, allow me to extend to you my best wishes for every success in here. Your vocation has shown itself to be firm. Let us hope that it will remain so in the future. The two years of the novitiate pass rapidly. There is no reason to feel fear and every reason to feel joy. The novitiate is a time dedicated exclusively to your spiritual formation. Nothing else will be allowed to distract you. The only distraction permitted will be the study of Latin and Greek . . . I congratulate you on the brief harsh test you have endured during the first days of isolation. This is the most dangerous of trials, because it is then that we are torn rudely from the world and abandoned to ourselves, to be besieged by memories. Many do not pass this test, and do not even reach the threshold of the novitiate itself . . . You must have felt very lonely during these days . . .'

'Oh, reverend father, never as much as in the world!'

The rector smiled, and Andrea understood the interview was over. As he took his leave, he bent to kiss his superior's hand, but the other drew it away brusquely.

'Among us,' he said, 'it is not the custom to kiss a priest's hand. This usage is reserved for the Father General of the Society. In future, after every interview with me or with the novice master, you will kneel and ask for a blessing. This is our holy custom.'

Andrea knelt down awkwardly. The father rector recited hurriedly the formula of the prayer over the young man, touched his hair with his hand and then led him gently to the door.

The morning was marked by a light, insistent drizzle. The robing ceremony took place in a gloomy atmosphere, unrelieved by the dim sparkle of the chapel golds, the dull sound of the organ, the dark shades of the old stones and the pallor of the faces surrounding Andrea. He loved that whole twilight world. There was in it a strange mixture of sensuality and devotion which mirrored the dominant, secret passions of his heart. From that sensuality contaminated by spirituality, there was born a veiled, irremediable form of corruption to which Andrea abandoned himself with a sort of rapture. From the young, smooth faces with their display of austere concentration, and from those vigorous, clean-shaven necks, there seemed to explode an uneasy hymn of tainted purity and closed, unfathomable melancholy.

During the entire time of the function, one thought beat insistently inside Andrea's mind, 'Today another life beckons you, other ways summon you . . .' He felt elegant in the long, black woollen robe with the silk sash around his waist, the new shoes and thousand-pleated cloak. That day's mass exalted all those who had, in the name of Christ, removed the things of this world from their hearts: the meek, the afflicted, the just, the merciful, the pure of heart, the peace-makers faced with persecutions. 'Rejoice,' said the Gospel, 'because great will be your reward in the kingdom of heaven.'

After the ceremony, Andrea followed the other novices into the apartment reserved for them. The various rooms used as dormitories, as library, as workshop for manual work, as classroom and as toilets opened off a wide corridor. He was put into a room with three novices whom he did not know. Hard wooden beds stood in the four corners of the room, with a table, a chair and a rough wooden prie-dieu beside each one. A small crucifix hung from the wall in front of each table. There were unadorned mobile screens to pull around the beds at night-time.

Andrea was happy to be with the other members of the community in those poor rooms and to participate in the severe timetable of the novitiate. In the mornings, at six o'clock precisely, a lay-brother passed from room to room to awaken the novices with the traditional formula. *Deo gratias*, to which the sleepy youths would reply: *Deo gratias et Mariae*. Getting up at six o'clock each morning in the cold was difficult. It was still dark but, as it is written in the Scriptures, 'Man must rise before the sunrise to have your blessing, O Lord, and before the appearance of the light to adore You.'

7

Immediately they jumped from their beds and folded back the thin mattress, the sheets and blankets. Afterwards, they hurried over to the sinks to wash and shave in cold water, facing the tiny mirrors.

At six-thirty, at the first peal of the bell, they returned to their rooms and knelt in front of their tables and crucifixes for the day's first meditation, dedicated to a topic they themselves had chosen the previous night. The meditation was to last one hour precisely. Still in the most absolute silence, the novices proceeded at seven-thirty to the college chapel for daily mass and communion. Afterwards, they remained another quarter of an hour on their knees for the 'thanksgiving'. Next, back in their own rooms, they sat down at their tables for the morning meditation. This examination lasted fifteen minutes, and consisted in a mnemonic review of the meditation to note any omissions, distractions or good fruits.

At eight-thirty, they all went down to the refectory on the ground floor for a breakfast of coffee and bread, taken in the most absolute silence, preceded and followed by community prayer recited aloud by the novices kneeling on the bare floor of the huge room. After the meal, they returned to the chapel for a brief visit to the Blessed Sacrament, then back to their apartment to tidy it from top to bottom: corridor, dormitories, library, classroom, workshop, toilets. This routine was followed by the office of the Blessed Virgin, recited in Latin as they walked in groups of two or three along the corridor or, when the weather was good, in the garden. In the early days, Andrea made many pronunciation mistakes and, when it came to the Psalms, he often put the accent in the wrong place, but his companions invariably pretended not to notice. Returning once again to their various rooms, the young men sat at their tables for the reading and study of the Constitutions of the

Order and the rules. The rules, which had been written personally by St Ignatius, had to be learned by heart, day after day. This study was followed by the reading of some passages from the *Imitation of Christ* and, finally, of the *Exercise of Perfection*, written by Rodriguez, a seventeenth-century Spanish ascetic who had been a member of the Society. At midday, at the sound of the bell, the whole community knelt down once again in their own rooms to undertake the day's first examination of conscience. This lasted a quarter of an hour and was to include every thought, word and deed formulated or undertaken by each one in the course of the morning.

In the early days, Andrea could not wait for the bell which marked the end of this exercise. When the bell rang, the young men met in a silent row to go down to the refectory on the ground floor. Unlike in the morning, this time they were joined by the whole community of the house: fathers, lay-brothers and the scholastics (these latter being the young men who had completed the two-year novitiate and were waiting to be posted elsewhere for the seven-year study of philosophy and theology). The community prayer was recited while standing, then each of them took his place at the long tables running along the walls of the room. During the meal, one of the novices would take his turn in the pulpit to read passages in Latin from the lives of the saints and pages from the Constitutions of the Society. After the prayer at the end of lunch, the whole community went to the chapel for a brief, silent prayer of thanksgiving. As they came out of chapel, the novices separated from the rest of the community and went back to their apartment, or else out into the garden, when the weather permitted it, for one hour's recreation.

Now, for the first time in the day, they were allowed to speak. One of the elders among the novices, who acted as head and moderator, divided them into groups of three or four, and for the entire period of recreation they were forbidden to move away from the companions assigned to them, to isolate themselves or to choose other companions. Their freedom to speak was not absolute. All were obliged to converse on prearranged topics, the same topics which a companion of Ignatius of Loyola, the Spanish father Nadal, had chosen for them centuries before. These conversation topics concerned exclusively the life of the novitiate, the history of the Church and of the Society, the examples of the saints, the principal vices and virtues of man, excepting those pertaining to chastity.

After recreation, the novitiate was once more immersed in the deepest silence. The young men, still in groups of three, recited the rosary and immediately afterwards, back in their rooms, did private reading from the pages of a spiritual book chosen freely from those in the library catalogues. At four o'clock, they were divided into groups again and left free for the daily walk, which lasted one hour, either in the vicinity of the house or in the lonely hills of Albano and Nemi. Except for Fridays, the day of the death of Christ, they were allowed to discuss the usual, prearranged topics. Back in the house, they took the afternoon snack in silence, then, for three-quarters of an hour, they studied Latin and Greek: Cicero's *De Officiis* and the New Testament. There followed, on certain days of the week, the 'spiritual exhortations' of the novice master: some days there was around an hour's manual work dedicated to the manufacture of the instruments of penitence (scourges and chains), other days practice in preaching from an improvised pulpit. At six-thirty, the bell rang to call the young men to the dormitories to kneel in front of their tables and crucifixes. Now it was time for the second meditation of the day, a half-hour in length. Later, when the beds had been prepared, the novices returned to the chapel where, together with the rest of the community, they recited the litanies of the Blessed Virgin and of the saints. From the chapel, in line and in hierarchical order, the community went down to the refectory and, after supper and a brief silent prayer of thanksgiving in the chapel, they once more went their separate ways. In their apartment, the novices enjoyed a half-hour's recreation, normally in groups of three but always with a different make-up. Some evenings, instead of recreation, there was the so-called 'quarter of an hour of charity', during which they met in the classroom for a mutual, public disclosure of sins.

At nine-fifteen, the bell called everyone to their own rooms for the day's second examination of conscience, which was conducted while kneeling and which covered all the inner and outer events of the afternoon and evening. At nine-thirty, at the peal of the bell, the young men sat down at their tables for the selection and preparation of the subject for the following day's morning meditation. At nine-forty-five, the bell rang once more and the whole community met in the chapel for the final community visit to the Blessed Sacrament. The lay-brothers and novices processed in first, followed by the scholastics, the superiors and, finally, the father rector. The father rector exited first, followed by the others, who processed from the chapel in inverse order to that in which they had entered. Back in their own rooms, the novices pulled the screens around their beds and undressed hurriedly. At ten o'clock precisely, a lay-brother passed from room to room to switch off the lights.

2

The first weeks were a time of happiness and enthusiasm for Andrea. He felt at ease, he put on weight and had no regrets over his past life. The company of the brothers made the novitiate seem a kind of new family, but a family without the endless bickering and quarrels common in families in the world. However, with the passing of time, he came to notice the development, even in his new family, of an obscure, complex, concealed network of resentments and repressed jealousies. He was still too much of a newcomer to that environment to be fully aware of everything, but he did understand that the novices kept each other under observation. At that stage, he kept his natural curiosity in check, especially during the periods of recreation. He gradually learned that he should never enter into a spirited discussion about anything: any such display would leave him open to reproach for lacking in humility. In truth, it became increasingly difficult for him to grasp the exact sense of this Christian virtue. His brothers asserted that it consisted simply in humiliations, but he was not particularly convinced. Equally, he eschewed the opinion of those in the world who tended to believe that humility meant pretty women striving to believe themselves ugly, or intelligent men doing their best to believe themselves stupid. For the moment, he gave up every attempt at resolving the problem, and limited himself to the observance of the most minute precepts which regulated the novices' day, in the conviction that this was, for him, the best and most sincere testimony which could be offered to humility. In the chapel, he kept his head absolutely still so as to avoid comments from the novice master, who had already had occasion to warn certain novices that they moved their heads this way and that too frequently. He avoided any unusual form of devotion. He understood immediately that the novice master would have no truck with mysticism, charisma or anything of that sort. He strove in particular to educate his will so as to render it absolute master of himself. Even during the daily walks, he was not permitted to abandon himself to any form of personal showiness, or even to raise his soutane too much. One of the 'unusual acts' for which Andrea was rebuked was for failing at table to tuck his napkin into the collar of his habit, as did all the others. He was to live the faith, his superiors taught him, not only as a simple submission of the intellect to revealed truths, but as the complete adherence of the entire man, mind and will, to Jesus Christ and to the Church.

He understood that, without humility, he was in a false position: he could know neither who he was nor what he owed others. He could not render to God or his neighbour what was theirs. The fruits of humility were calm, contentment, peace with God and man, and graciousness towards everyone. Humility was the foundation of the spiritual life, the easiest way and the best preparation for all that was most painful in the acquisition of the virtues.

But how could humility, true humility, fail to recognize or fail to acknowledge one's own gifts and talents? Andrea was convinced that humility, without vain self-glorification, should enable all talents to be addressed to God, from whom they came. One day, he went to see his novice master to set out to him the doubts which were causing him such turmoil. The superior pulled from a drawer in his desk a reproduction in colour of a fresco by Giotto, and handed it to him.

'Giotto was one of the first to understand this fundamental virtue,' he said. 'It has been subjected to such variations in the popular mind that even today everyone speaks of it, but hardly anyone is capable of saying what it consists of. Those who have something to say on the subject will assert that the pinnacle of Christian humility lies in the constant and eager longing to turn the eyes away from one's own ego, on account of the danger of discovering one's own merits and taking pleasure in them . . .'

The priest interrupted himself, and smiled.

'We Jesuits,' he went on, 'have never accepted this negative idea of humility, this flight from the self as though it were an unclean spectacle. No, none of that has ever been able to raise a single person to that inner grandeur with which the genuinely humble have always been abundantly endowed. Once it was different: in the holy faces depicted by our painters in the fourteenth century, and later by all the most famous artists of the following two centuries, it is easy to identify the common opinion of these great centuries as regards humility. An idea deriving from Dante and St Francis had taken root among the people, an idea which held that the title "Humble Lady" given to Beatrice expressed all grandeur and ardour, and signified the highest exaltation of which the earthly creature was capable. The fact is that humility was conceived in a positive form as advance and not as flight, as an act of confidence and not as a tangle of precautions. That concept went into decline when it seemed to split apart, under the impact of the Reformation and the Catholic reaction to it, into two constituent elements, which in their turn degenerated to the point where one of them, human perfection, was transmuted into vanity, and the other, the relationship with God, into mere humiliation, into joined hands, lowered eyes and all that unctuosity typical of faces painted with self-conscious contrition. Humility had been transformed into humiliation, and even into the mask of downright hypocrisy.'

Silence fell. Then the priest, speaking quietly, added, 'We Jesuits too must bear part of the responsibility for this degeneration of humility, but St Ignatius and the early fathers of the Society can act as models for us. They did prepare the Counter-Reformation, but they must not be considered responsible for all that derived from it. St Ignatius loved above all things the happy medium, the golden virtue of discretion. He went so far as to say that those who were not fit for the world could not be regarded as fit for the Society. "The man who shows himself most able in the world," he was accustomed to say, "that man is best suited for us."'

Andrea always tried to behave graciously towards the other novices, even when they, more or less deliberately, showed the more unsavoury sides of their characters. When he chose, Andrea knew the secret of making himself loved, because in this world the only way to be loved was to appear affable. Affability was a great conciliator, and disarmed even arrogance, spite and envy. Brother Zanna was undoubtedly the finest mind in the novitiate. He had both taste and tact. Andrea thought that there could be many people who had taste but not tact, or vice versa, because it was easy to possess the one without the other. If taste was a feeling for moral and physical beauty, tact was an instinct for propriety. Tact was generally a product of education and, sooner or later, no Jesuit was likely to be found wanting on that front. Taste, on the other hand, could be formed in conversation and acquired by frequenting people equipped with it. Andrea noticed that the fathers with whom he lived were invariably people of tact, and often of taste, and he considered it a privilege to be able to live in an environment of that sort and at a level scarcely attainable in the world.

The conversations he had had with the novice master had revealed a man possessed of a fascinating, melancholy sense of life. That man must have learned how to observe his fellow men with that wide measure of human sympathy which transcended the narrow horizons of enthusiasm and of satire, and which was the indefinable, all-revealing quality of certain rare individuals. He provided an uninterrupted, unfailingly accessible lesson in civility, courtesy, measure, love and respect for one's neighbour. That man did not appear to Andrea to be a factious or partisan man, as he had elsewhere heard the Jesuits described. On the question of humility, he had told Andrea things which had filled him with admiration and which seemed to him imbued with discretion. In addition, his very external appearance seemed to confirm the gifts which Andrea attributed to him. He did not bring to mind the image of a spoiled saint, nor of a Pharisee, inquisitor or magus, categories of person whom Andrea considered worse than any tyrant or any common sinner. That director of souls had a proud reserve, a slightly alienating distinction, together with a simplicity without affectation, all of which pleased Andrea. The priest seemed endowed with a discreet piety oriented towards the active life, and this activity, which must have cost him dear, seemed achieved without effort, but with an archaic, atavistic elegance transmitted from generation to generation from the first disciples of St Ignatius.

Not everything in the progress of the religious life satisfied Andrea, but his dissatisfaction did not lead him to the door of the novice master. At the outset, self-mortification had not seemed to him unduly onerous. At table, practically no fasting was required of him. There was abstinence on Fridays, but it consisted in giving up one of the many courses on offer, the choice being left to the individual. The obligation not to isolate oneself during periods of recreation, either on one's own or, even worse, with one other novice, or with companions different from those who had been assigned to him, irritated Andrea, and he often suffered small outbreaks of inner rage, which he immediately mastered and to which no one around him seemed to pay any heed. Being deprived of money, his watch and the other personal accessories which he had been in the habit of carrying with him did cause him some annoyance. They would be returned to him only at the end of his novitiate, and the money not even then. In the last analysis, it was those apparently negligible details of the religious life which upset him, rather than its rigour or the denial of material comforts, such as the freezing water in the morning or the boards on which he had to sleep. On the contrary, he boasted to himself about these things, even if he knew that vainglory had been called by the saints 'spiritual lust'.

In time, the routine corporal penances, without becoming completely intolerable to him, came to seem senseless, cruel acts of torture. He noticed that it was not only him, but all the other novices, who greeted announcements of these penances with evident signs of boredom and annoyance. The thirst for renunciation and for sacrifice was genuine in each of them, and yet they drew back from the prospect of acts of external mortification. They would make their way to their own rooms with no enthusiasm and go behind the screens, the appointed place of the collective penances. Their obedience was exclusively of the will as, to the sound of the bell in the darkness, each one flagellated himself for a few seconds. The advice given to them was to flog the soft part of the body; they were severely prohibited from inflicting on themselves blows of such a violence as to cause the rupture of tissue and the shedding of blood. Andrea emerged from those flagellations profoundly humiliated, all trembling nerves and taut resentment. A penitence of this sort, carried out without reference to the psychic dispositions of the individual at any given moment, seemed to him absurd. Everything was effected rapidly, with a mechanical indifference which, if it did demonstrate a salutary agility of the will, provoked in the long term a state of tension which was anything but normal.

The so-called discipline, that is, self-flagellation, occurred three times a week with rope instruments which the novices themselves had manufactured during the time assigned to manual work. Another form of penitence, equally degrading for Andrea, was the penitence of the chains, a sort of iron bracelet and leg-brace with sharp points, which the novices tightened around their wrist and leg three times a week, during the hour of the morning meditation. These instruments of mortification too were manufactured by the young men during manual work, both for the internal use of the community and to meet the demand of the numerous religious houses, male or female, scattered in the zone of the Castelli Romani.

One evening, it was Andrea's turn to be protagonist of the so-called 'quarter of an hour of charity', one of the most debilitating and formal exercises of the novitiate. He was completely worn out, and could find no comfort in an encouraging phrase from the novice master, who told him, 'Fatigue is useful, since it produces extreme gentleness and mental calm and even produces something resembling vision.' He was not of this opinion when he discovered that he had been chosen for the 'quarter of an hour of charity'. He was tense and scarcely inclined to gentleness as, with all the nonchalance he could summon, he entered the classroom used for the event. As he had seen other more elderly novices do before him, he moved into the centre of the room, knelt down and kissed the ground in front of the novice master, while his brothers stood around him in a circle. Then with his hands joined, in silence, he listened patiently for a quarter of an hour without being allowed to speak a single word while his brothers, one after the other, declaimed, in charity and truth, all the defects and shortcomings noted in him. There was one who reproached him for an excessive spirit of criticism and independence. When it came to Brother Zanna's turn, there was an edge of emphasis and irony in his voice as he drew attention to the fact that he had dared read a few pages of a book in the refectory, during the morning meal. Another novice observed his repeated breaches of silence and of punctuality, yet another attacked his lack of patience on certain given occasions, and finally another lamented the fact that he had not always observed the library regulations, and had the deplorable habit of writing in pencil in the books he had out on loan.

This kind of charity had long disturbed Andrea. He thought that the purpose of this penitence was to depress the novice and, until the wise teaching of the superiors intervened to re-establish balance, make him feel ill at ease with himself and with others. Andrea remembered an observation which Brother Zanna had made casually one day during recreation: 'The method of the carrot and stick is a method not unknown to the famous *ratio studiorum*, the *magna charta* of Jesuit pedagogy.' Its purpose was to produce, through a system of rivalries and ambitions which were raised, suppressed and revived once again, men militant for the Church and for the Society. On the other side of the scales, the Jesuits placed little titbits, images of saints, all the various feasts of the domestic and religious calendar during which the so-called culinary 'caresses' alternated with the 'academies', that is, erudite and pedantic performances which gave the young men the opportunity to flaunt themselves innocently with doggerel in Latin metre, chaste little ditties and comic or sentimental sketches.

However, after a couple of months, Andrea was persuaded that the worst penitence of religious life was life in the company of people of a wholly different personality, who could be in turn harsh and discourteous. A day-by-day, hour-by-hour, minute-by-minute penitence.

Andrea had succeeded in liberating himself from the century's most senseless traits and practices: smoking, drinking, cinema-going, reading pornographic magazines or books which be-smirch the heart and wearing fashionable clothes. There was as much solidity in the life he was now leading as in the wholewheat bread he ate, in the grape wine he drank or in the violent and candid attitudes of his companions. And he revelled in the biographies of the saints: the discovery of a new saint was a stupendous experience. Each saint was different from the next. Unfortunately, most of the time he could only lay his hands on those hagiographies which were a chain of fantastic miracles interspersed with devout commonplaces. For some of Andrea's more exuberant brothers, the term 'spiritual reading' had decidedly dismal overtones, and the fact that the religious life was something divided into exercises caused them bouts of depression. Andrea had entered the religious life resigned to the prospect of having to listen for the rest of his life to one particular kind of devout language and to a rhetoric, common in religious houses, capable of literally causing trembling fits in some people.

And it was just as well that he and his other companions, like Brother Zanna, were so resigned, because one of the most tedious aspects of the monastic life was receiving the greater part of their spiritual nourishment in the flat and insipid jargon of the manual of piety. Of the standard words in the vocabulary of many novices, the one which most irritated Andrea was 'consoling'. It seemed to him that some of them, whose scrupulousness in attempting to comply with every regulation produced a deformed reality, went over the score in everything they did. Others gave evidence of such disturbance of the nervous system that they abandoned themselves to demonstrations of morbid bigotry. Andrea had occasion to watch several of his brothers reach out for the holy water font which was to be found in every room in the house, and make the sign of the cross each time they entered a room. That could happen up to twenty times in the course of a few minutes. This deviation had been pointed out to the novice master, who had had to intervene more than once to moderate the intemperate fervour of those young men. One of them soaked his bed in holy water every evening, so as, as he put it, to ward off temptation. Some form of reticence was common to all of them, because they were enjoined never to think of the past but to pretend to forget and ignore it. In reality, this complex past of theirs, with its confusions, misunderstandings and errors, was so much present that there was no need to allude to it: it was a past which had brought only bewilderment, anxiety, incomprehension and outbursts of irritation to each one of them.

Andrea believed he had accumulated a deeper wealth of experience than most of the others, but he was mistaken: all of them, even the youngest, carried with them a portmanteau of adventures which fully matched his. He became aware that those boys had attempted in the past to respond to everything that life could offer their generation: cinemas, dance halls, cheap little bars on the outskirts of the major cities, and those other sad, glittering, typically twentieth-century establishments, with their glow of pink and violet neon lights. Others had been to university and talked among themselves about how they had managed to attend university for four years without suffering spiritually or morally. Moreover, they were free from those shoddy prejudices common among those whose only thoughts were of cars, films, of what was in the refrigerator or written in colour supplements. At times, some of them would let slip some confidential remark from which it was easy to deduce that they had been happy and fulfilled, had gone dancing and had been full of ambitious ideas and projects. But things had not, 'thanks be to God', taken the turn they had initially desired, and now it was all over. For them too, people had come and gone in their young lives. They had had different friends at different times. There were some names they all thought of, in secret. But faith had saved them, and now they clung tightly to it: they believed more strongly than the theologians required men to believe as 'medium requirement'. Each and every one of them was in a condition of spiritual convalescence.

Apart from these affinities, what weighed each of them down most strongly was their life in common. It happened quite frequently that one of them would have a tone of voice or an expression of face which became almost intolerably irritating to someone else. So as not to be found wanting in charity, they were obliged to master themselves and appear friendly to everyone, even to those who had the knack of coming up with those insidious little phrases which could ruin an entire day. 'In every soul,' the novice master warned them, 'there will always be a little benevolence mingled with a little malice. The important thing for the devil is to direct the malevolence towards our immediate neighbours, towards those whom a man will meet on a daily basis, and to chase the benevolence to some far-off land, towards people whom we do not know. Malevolence will thus become perfectly real and benevolence largely imaginary.' In this matter too, it was the will which was to act as guide, but not that will which they knew only too well, expressed as a nervous irritation of resolutions and clenched teeth, but the genuine core of the will: the heart.

Several times a day, thinking of where he was, Andrea would repeat to himself the words of the apostle: 'Lord, it is good for us to be here.' There was no aversion in him towards the life he had embraced, but he seemed to understand, for the first time, that plans made for the service of God could never be accomplished without great suffering. When, after the discovery of his flight and of the refuge to which he had withdrawn, the young man's family came to visit him, they appeared worried about the motives which they believed had driven him to the religious life: a moment of difficulty, of weakness or despair. The malign wisdom of the people came easily to their lips: 'Despair breeds the majority of monks and priests.' Andrea did not know if he had ever experienced despair. Exhausted of the life he had been leading, he had desired no more than to search out a secure path. Faith had arrived, or returned, at the right moment. The apprehension expressed by his relatives made him laugh. The words of the Gospel came to his mind: 'The kingdom of heaven suffers force, and wild and violent men snatch it away.'

Even if not all aspects of his new life gave him satisfaction, even if many elements of it appeared to him formal and cruel, there was a clarity to the existence he was now leading. He understood that the principal thing in the novitiate was education for the life of the spirit. The sole purpose of it all was to make the impact of this initiation deep and lasting. The separation of the novices from the rest of the community, their uninterrupted silence for almost the whole of the day, the lengthy prayers, the instruction and the reports, the exercises of outer, and even more of inner, mortification, in a word, all that purified the soul and helped it to progress in the knowledge of the divine Lord, were all appropriate means employed with loving rigour. The novice was obliged to submit not only to the general rule of the Order but also to a number of special regulations, each calculated to loosen, from morning to night, the grip of self-love and egoism. That life, seen in its entirety, was a weight which could not but seem unbearable even for the broadest back. The profane who came to visit Andrea did not seem to be aware of what enormous tension of the will, what incessant mastery of the self, such a life was bound to exact. Andrea, for his part, did all he could to ensure that, in spite of the atrocious, systematic control of himself, a certain spiritual agility survived in him.

One day, his mother had burst into tears when she saw him in the parlour. And that futile, female weeping had seemed to Andrea like a chorus of music in a military encampment. He had observed how his mother stared at him as though he were a rare animal, or an involuntary detainee, a galley slave. The habit which the young man was wearing seemed to put a great distance between them, and gave him an authority he did not deserve. And when the woman expounded hesitantly her worries that her son was living in a state contrary to nature, he reacted swiftly. He protested, with a touch of exaggeration, that he was not subject to any violent servitude or any restriction of his innermost aspirations. He did admit that, to do and observe everything his superiors demanded or desired of him, he required a spiritual strength which could only be replenished by gigantic reserves of inner enthusiasm and energy. The most evangelical endowment of the soul was strength.

After that interview, Andrea had no wish to see again anyone from the outside world, not even his closest relatives. His superiors acceded to his wish, even if it appeared excessive to several of them.

3

There was one brother for whom Andrea believed he felt a secret love, a love he did not consider altogether stainless. He loved Brother Zanna too, but that was different: theirs was principally an intellectual friendship, in part loving, but with no taint of carnality. The rational affection which Andrea bore towards Zanna was born from a feeling of justified admiration, while the desire which drove him to seek out and to gaze for long periods at the other brother derived from an unruly sentiment of the heart. From the beginning, he was afraid of his own feelings and, knowing the aversion of his own superiors for so-called special friendships, and the severity on this point of the treatises of ascetics (including the treatise by Rodriguez, adopted by the novitiate), he went one day to discuss the matter with his novice master.

The priest listened to him for a long time in silence, then with a fatherly smile, said to him, 'You must not trouble yourself for so little. It is clear that the human heart cannot live without some attachments of the senses. It is, in other words, inevitable that you young people in here should seek each other out, unconsciously, in accordance with mutual affections and inclinations. But the important thing is to dominate all inner longings, to suffocate them, to destroy them, when they offend charity. If you feel an irregular fondness for Brother Lodovici, the virtue of charity towards the other brothers, not to mention natural reason itself, will both suggest that you should stay as far away from him as possible, that you should avoid him and should, on the contrary, seek out the company of those other novices who appear more disagreeable, less likeable, to you. St Bernard says that the human heart is like a millstone which is continually grinding, but it is up to the miller to decide whether it should grind wheat or barley or something else. That is the nature of the human heart: it cannot stop grinding. However, it is up to us to decide if it will grind wheat or barley or earth. We must exercise caution. There exist some fires which, as St Paul said, burn but give off no light.'

These words fell like balm on the heart of Andrea, but were of little value to him in the following days. His nights were no longer peaceful. He lay hour after hour with his eyes open, listening to the calm, rhythmic breathing of the brothers who shared the room with him. He was frequently besieged by temptations against purity. Lewd images attacked and tormented him. Then, in the morning, he would rise exhausted from these sleepless jousts against everything that was most base and coarse in the human instinct.

He was amazed that the novice master never addressed to him any questions on chastity, since this was a burning problem for all those young men enclosed together in there. It was like a conspiracy of silence which seemed, little by little, to discourage any wish for openness or quest for information on the subject. 'The least said the better' seemed to be the motto of the superiors, and Andrea long remained in a state of bewilderment. Then he understood that they simply wished to sidle round the obstacle rather than tackle it head-on: this was the tactic, the operational plan. Everyone would have to fend for himself, or leave the Society.

Then Andrea realized, quite suddenly, that none of the men to whom he had spoken about his vocation knew who he was.

They knew nothing about his past, and took no interest in it. They had accepted him because he had a decent appearance, seemed sincere and sufficiently endowed with common sense and good will. On some days, he thought it was impossible that anyone except a madman could consider him fit for the priesthood. And yet that was how it was; he had all the qualities, according to the superiors, to be able to go forward in the novitiate and bring it to a successful completion. However, if he had ever imagined that he had won himself some immunity from the passions, or would not again have to struggle to be free of them, he could no longer entertain any illusions in that regard. And such was the deep fear that seized him over his own unworthiness that at times a terrible suspicion was born in him: on certain nights, it would seem that nothing remained of his vocation but a pile of ashes.

He found some comfort when he looked around him. He was struck by the fact that some of his brothers, particularly the younger ones, would pass from moments of exuberant joy to moments of dark depression. He thought that this derived from a sexual life which was either unduly repressed or too unnatural and disordered. He even went so far as to say to himself that an act of open fornication must be, in the eyes of God, less blameworthy than an impure, unwanted, miserable loss of chastity.

On the other hand, he had succeeded, with dreadful effort, in remaining chaste in there. Had that been down to his own strength? Was what the superiors frequently repeated true, that chastity was a virtue of will-power? Jesuits had always given great importance to free human will, as Andrea knew. But he also knew that passage in the Book of Wisdom which, on the contrary, stated, 'None can be continent unless You allow it.' Once again, irreducibly and insolubly, the opposing alternatives were determinism and free will.

Outside, in the world, he had managed to remain chaste for long periods. Inside, it had been much easier, considering the regime he was obliged to follow. But how he had been able to resist so long remained a mystery. Those first months of religious life had been nothing but a long succession of nocturnal pollutions provoked, every time, by libidinous dreams. He believed that it had been the same for everyone, or at least for those who had preserved the awesome virtue of chastity. If he, long known as a pleasure-seeker, had managed to keep himself pure, how much easier should it have been to overcome concupiscence for those of his brothers who had never had any carnal experience, or whose experience had been furtive and brief, leaving scarcely a trace in the memory and therefore untroubling and easily suppressed.

Nevertheless, there came a night when Andrea was guilty of a solitary fall from purity. He was gripped by such shame and anxiety that he immediately jumped from his bed, threw on his clothes and went to bang repeatedly on the door of the novice master. A few moments later, the priest opened the door: he appeared as calm and as meticulously dressed as ever, although the pallor and swelling of his face testified to the brusque manner of his arousal from sleep.

The superior understood that something serious had occurred. Instead of inviting Andrea into his room, he led him silently into the garden. It was late and cold. With bowed head, Andrea confessed his sin. In the faint light, worn out by an overwhelming, inner strain which gnawed away at him, he looked like a small, primitive idol. Beside his superior, he felt exposed and naked, like a fishbone from which all the flesh had been pared away. And never so strongly as at that moment had he felt such a deep awareness of belonging to a category of intermediate, ambiguous and exiled beings.

From the Via Appia came the solitary singing of an old folk song, full of subtle, elegiac cadenzas. The fragile motifs of those despairing rhythms came together, broke apart only to link up once more. The flowing water of the fountain in the garden nearby splashed in gurgling jets. After Andrea's hurried confession, the novice master remained silent. The young man, disturbed by that obstinate taciturnity, tried frantically to rekindle the flickering flames of thought in his mind and to find some word to break the silence. Finally, the priest said, in a flat, impersonal voice, 'My son, the custody of chastity is not something impossible. Here too, it is the fact of will-power which counts most . . . It's only a question of the continual training of the will, that's all there is to it.'

Andrea did not stop to consider how irreverent his reply might appear: 'And grace, father, where do you put grace?'

'The will too is the daughter of grace.'

They both fell silent as they walked up and down the avenue leading to the fountain. Their footsteps crackled on the gravel path.

'You have too much imagination,' said the novice master, 'and those who have much imagination are exposed to a multitude of temptations, because the imagination is prone to revive in them the original sensations of which it is no more than an extension. Moreover, it heightens and diversifies those renewed sensations in a thousand ways. In order to obtain purity of the body, my son, you must, first and foremost, safeguard the purity of the heart, the mind and the eyes. The custody of the senses is a categorical imperative, particularly the custody of the eyes, that most delicate of all the senses, because from it the entire, dangerous potency of the visual memory derives. There is a difference between seeing and looking. If we cannot prevent ourselves from seeing, we must none the less aim to be successful in not looking, in other words in avoiding that constancy of the attention which we might call "assiduity of the eyes". What matters always is to maintain self-control through continual analysis and mastery of inner inclinations.'

There was a pause. The novice master stopped at the bottom of the pathway, under the thick darkness of a holm oak.

'You must develop the habit,' he continued, 'of uniting the vivacity of mental representations with a disposition towards reflection. You must learn to block image with image, so as to pre-empt the risk of further lapses. If you succeed in facing up to those suggestions which are familiar to you, you will in a sense wear them out, head off any consequences and give yourself prior experience of all their fruits, whether refreshing or poisonous.'

'But it is so difficult, father.'

'You must familiarize yourself with the theory of the discernment of spirits of our holy father, St Ignatius. You must learn to recognize immediately the images, thoughts and ideas which follow one another and take each other's place inside you. You must observe how they present themselves to you and how they can be dismissed. Ideas of holiness are good thoughts not only because they are in conformity with religious law, but also because they fortify the soul, they console it, they fill it, as it were, with solid nourishment: on the contrary, the others – the ideas of vanity, of self-love, or of sensuality – even if they seem pleasing at the moment when you embrace them, will quickly disperse, leaving the soul empty and unsatisfied. It is not in anyone's power, my boy, to be always dominated by good ideas, but every one of us is capable of choosing the moment when he will undergo their influence, and so of making decisive resolutions and, with the assistance of the will, of persevering with them through thick and thin. The important thing is to train the will by continual exercises.'

'The will is weak, father, and sometimes I feel so discouraged . . .'

'Even discouragement is pride,' said the superior. As they re-entered the house, he invited the novice into the chapel to pray. They knelt down, their elbows lightly touching, and remained for a few minutes still and in silence.

The novice master wished to accompany Andrea to the threshold of the novices' apartment. He addressed him once again, in a whisper. 'Go in peace, my son, sleep peacefully. Remember that Christianity was God's greatest act of boldness on earth. And the Church is so convinced of this that it has always shown itself infinitely tolerant of the sins of the flesh. But it is unyielding with sins of pride. I do not believe that hell is for those unfortunates who obeyed, more or less cautiously, the law of nature, who fell under the recurrent curse of original sin, who were struck down by the fleeting enchantment of the flesh. Hell is for the proud of heart, who are often sexually cold and who have never seen themselves as creatures of a Creator. They commit the most abominable of sins, the sin which brought into the world death, pain and work: the sin of pride.'

'Work, father?'

'Certainly, work as well. It is the modern ideologies that have attempted to exalt and ennoble work. Nonsense! Christianity has always considered work a curse, one of the many sentences passed on man after the first fall. I believe that all real workers are more likely to agree, in the depth of their hearts, with the wisdom of the Church on this point. And now go in peace, my son, and do not forget confession tomorrow morning before holy mass and communion.'

Before climbing into bed, Andrea hurriedly scribbled out these few lines on a sheet of paper: 'Of the seven deadly sins, only the first is genuinely deadly. From pride, in fact, the seven principal and most ruinous vices are born: vainglory, arrogance, ambition, presumption, hypocrisy, obstinacy in one's own judgement and contempt of others.'

On some days, Brother Zanna seemed unduly restive and Andrea tried in vain to find some way of identifying the causes of his unease. He could not get close to him, and then, for days, Brother Zanna would keep him at bay, dodging his questions and pretending to have overcome or not even to remember his earlier disquiet. Finally one day, when the young man's spirits seemed particularly low, Andrea had the opportunity to accompany him on the afternoon walk. His persistent questioning, together with the fact that the third companion on the walk seemed to have no interest in their conversation, nor even to grasp much of it, goaded Zanna to talk. That day, Andrea discovered something which later began to disturb him too.

'I am becoming aware,' Brother Zanna had told him, 'that our vocation as novices does not permit the development of a human, cultural and social vocation in the wider context of the religious vocation. The legitimate means to live up to this natural vocation as well as to the other are denied us, which means that the relative material poverty which the rule makes us accept is the most trivial of sacrifices when compared to the intellectual poverty which the religious life forces on us. The impossibility of developing the natural vocations of my personality in the context of the religious vocation is causing me a great deal of pain.'

Andrea tried to console him by expressing agreement. 'I too,' he said, 'feel this emptiness, this impotence. But perhaps, brother, this is something which will last only for the two years of the novitiate, two years dedicated exclusively to our spiritual formation. Then, during the years of education in philosophy and theology, everything will be different.'

'I hope so,' replied Brother Zanna. 'In the meantime, there are many questions I ask myself and cannot answer. I cannot fail to recognize that there is a complete set, or perhaps a scale, of material, technical, economic, social, political and cultural factors which, left to themselves, have been made into the gravest of obstacles to the supernatural life: I mean, they make up a world which is closed and even hostile to the work of the Church. The problem is knowing if we will be able to renounce this world in which we have lived, the world which is after all responsible for our education.'

'Oh, for the moment we have to think only of our souls, not of these problems. Later on, brother, later on!'

'But will it not then be too late? You know, brother,' said Brother Zanna, 'some days I feel like all the prisoners in all the prisons in the world: at some moments, I see the sky and the earth through, if not exactly bars, certainly the grates of our house; and I ask myself, how could I, in the future, transform, stir up this "inane and dark" world (as the novice master defines it) to which I do not belong?'

'The superiors, brother,' replied Andrea, 'will be able to show us the way and the means. We are Jesuits and we are called to do nothing other than obey.'

34

'All right, but the very men who personify these theories, our superiors, are too cold, paternal and distant. I am convinced that each of us will have to resolve by himself, in the intimacy of his own conscience, a certain number of problems.'

Andrea was afraid that the other novice in their company might have grasped how subversive and unorthodox Brother Zanna's statements were, but he walked a few steps ahead of them, his eyes fixed on the ground, apparently absorbed in prayer or in something else. The conversation seemed to hold no interest for him. There was a long pause. However much he admired Brother Zanna, Andrea could not help noticing in him a kind of cold, collected, intellectual pride which had nothing in common with that dull light in the dark, that strength in weakness, that virtue in silence and those modest, severe practices which he so admired in Brother Lodovici. On the way back, the conversation turned to the last 'exhortation' addressed to them the preceding day by the novice master. So as to point out his contradictions, Andrea reminded Brother Zanna of the superior's words when he declared that the Society aimed at the creation of all-round men, lacking in nothing. In other words, the formation of Jesuits guaranteed the full, harmonious development of the human personality.

'You have a tendency, brother,' explained Andrea, 'to give undue importance to the full development of the human person on the natural rather than on the supernatural plane. In the world, one of these two planes is sacrificed: in it, the development of the personality takes no account of God.'

'Here, on the contrary,' replied Brother Zanna, 'it is easy sometimes to get the impression that the other plane, the natural plane, is sacrificed. In both cases, the development of personality is only partial.'

'But the saints were complete men,' said Andrea, 'and the

development of the personality in them was complete both on the supernatural and on the natural plane.'

'Yes, but in the Church, the saints represent the exception, not the rule.' They fell silent for a brief moment, then Brother Zanna started up again.

'To tell you the truth, I did not even find the "exhortations" of the novice master on the figure of Jesus totally persuasive. The interpretation he offered of Christ was unduly unilateral, too much in harmony with the spirit of the Society. I love this spirit, but I have also a deep knowledge of the Gospels. When I was thirteen, I already knew them by heart.'

'By heart?' asked Andrea in amazement.

Brother Zanna went on, 'If it is true that any concept of a historical Christ which clashes with the Catholic tradition is false, and if it is true that recent generations have promoted the construction of a supposed historical Jesus along liberal and humanitarian lines, and now are putting together a new historical Christ in keeping with a Marxist, catastrophic, revolutionary scheme, it is equally true that it is difficult to accept totally the representation of Christ put forward by the novice master. He made use of each and every episode in the Gospels to justify the history of the Society, warts and all, as well as to justify the spirit, which is at times downright Machiavellian, of our Constitutions . . .'

Brother Zanna was growing more and more heated. At this point, the other brother who made up the threesome seemed also to be listening, aghast. Andrea intervened in some alarm.

'You're surely exaggerating, brother: the term "Machiavellian" seems to me completely out of order, in this case.'

Brother Zanna did not reply right away. A little later he smiled and said, 'Oh well, after Machiavelli everything, or at least nearly everything, in the world has taken on a slightly

Machiavellian appearance. The only one who was not Machi-avellian was Machiavelli himself. A real Machiavellian would never have written a treatise on Machiavellianism.'

All three burst out laughing at this conclusion, and their laughter lowered the tension which had been building up. The conversation turned to other matters.

The following day, during the afternoon recreation, Andrea and Brother Zanna were summoned by the father rector. In the room they also found the novice master, on his feet, wearing an expression of the deepest affliction.

When the two novices were seated facing him, the father rector came straight to the point, stating that he was aware of the conversation the two young men had had the previous day during their afternoon walk. Andrea did not appear to be facing charges related to the opinions outlined in the course of that conversation, these opinions being attributed to Brother Zanna, but he was considered blameworthy for having failed to make an immediate report to the novice master.

'I did not believe that they were quite so serious,' lied Andrea.

The father rector rebuked him severely, observing that his willingness to produce such a shabby justification as an excuse meant that he must so far have assimilated very little of the spirit of the Society. Brother Zanna, the real accused, attempted to explain himself.

'Reverend father, when I defined the Constitutions of St Ignatius as Machiavellian, I had genuinely no thought either of diminishing or of compromising their grandeur or sanctity; on the contrary, it was my intention to emphasize their value in the struggle which the Society has been conducting for centuries for the triumph of the Church Militant –'

'You, my boy,' interrupted the father rector, 'belong to that category of person, normally enemies of ours, who claim to identify in the Constitutions even things which are not there at all. You want to show off your own deep insight, and instead all you do is come up with rash judgements, not to say acts of blasphemy.'

The superior, raising his voice, went on, 'I'll bet you even believe in the *Monita Secreta*!'

'Oh no, reverend father,' replied Brother Zanna, 'it's easy to prove they're a forgery.'

'Have you read that pamphlet?' asked the father rector.

'Yes,' replied Brother Zanna, 'before entering the novitiate.'

'What impression did it make on you?'

'I wondered what it was that created such a fuss, or that gave rise to such lengthy, tedious polemics. It is all so puerile and contentious . . . The story that there really could be such a thing as the *Monita Secreta* in possession of our Father General doesn't stand up.'

'And yet, with your observations yesterday, you came close to insinuating that the practice of the Society mirrors, at least in part and superficially, the theories of the apocryphal pamphlet of the Polish ex-Jesuit. You seemed to imply that the *Monita Secreta* might be a caricature of the true sense with which each word of the holy Constitutions of St Ignatius is imbued.'

'No, reverend father, I had absolutely no intention of reaching any such conclusion. I realize that I used certain words without being fully aware of their meaning: I realize I have made a fool of myself.'

There was a pause. Andrea noticed that the novice master was suffering more than any of them in that room.

'I understand,' the rector began again, 'that you even dared criticize the "exhortations" of the novice master who is here with us. Do you realize that the spirit of independence which you have demonstrated towards the superiors is sufficient reason for your definitive expulsion from the novitiate and from the Society? I would still be in favour of this if the novice master had not interceded with me in your favour . . .'

Brother Zanna began to weep silently. Andrea lowered his eyes to the ground, but the father rector turned to him and invited him to say something, to explain the sense of the other subjects discussed during the previous day's walk.

'From what I was able to understand,' said Andrea, 'Brother Zanna stated that you have no right to direct the devotion of men and women towards something that does not exist, because no historical Jesus can be historical. The documents say what they say: you may or may not believe them, but you cannot add anything to them. In the second place, all these constructs base the importance of their historical Jesus on some theory they imagine he has promulgated. In the third place, by means of these constructs, the devout life is destroyed. Instead of the real presence of God, experienced by men only in prayer or in the sacraments, there is substituted a remote, shadowy, probable figure who spoke a strange language, intelligible only to initiates or to the supposed followers of his spirit. A subject of this kind, according to Brother Zanna, can be admired but not venerated. Instead of the Creator adored by his creatures, there emerges a distinguished personage, appreciated by judicious historians or, maybe, by learned Jesuits . . .'

'So then,' the father rector came close to yelling, 'we offer a partial, or maybe even false, image of Our Lord, *ad usum delphini* . . .'

'No, reverend father, Brother Zanna certainly did not mean to say this.'

39

'The novice master,' concluded the superior, 'will devote special attention to you in the days to come, and will attempt to straighten out your ideas. I myself will keep an eye on you in future. For the moment, you do not seem to me in any way novices permeated by the authentic spirit of St Ignatius, a spirit made up principally of obedience, but obedience which is not only external but also internal, mental. Remember that a Jesuit has no personal opinions, has no liberty of judgement. He thinks along with his superiors, in conformity with their will. The divine will is transmitted to each of us through legitimate authority, through a chain of hierarchy. Either we are able to accept this holy servitude, or else we are free, while there is still time, to return to the world. The novitiate is a time for the trial of the Order by the novice, and of the novice by the Order. Always bear this in mind.'

The rector fell silent, seemed to reflect for a few moments before adding, in a quiet voice, 'As a penance, you will recite the anonymous statement of guilt this evening in the refectory in front of the whole community. In addition, you will yourselves request the novice master to impose such other acts of penance as you yourselves personally will consider appropriate. You may go, my sons.'

The two young men knelt on the ground. The father rector blessed them, then dismissed them.

Later that evening Andrea was summoned for an interview with the novice master. Where the rector had shown himself unbendingly severe, the spiritual director showed himself gentle and paternal.

'Oh Andrea,' he said to him, 'do you realize the wrong you have done to Jesus, offending in him our holy father Ignatius, your superiors as well as the innocent ears of the brother who was accompanying you yesterday? That novice believed he

40

was doing his duty, in accordance with the spirit of the rule, by coming immediately to inform me of what he had overheard . . .'

'I can only beg your forgiveness, father. On another occasion I will make it my duty to come immediately to report everything to you.'

'Everything, my son, certainly: everything good and ill. Of this I am sure. But it will be more important to avoid in the future similar occasions of disobedience and sin. This action of yours, as you know, has wounded me deeply because I am well aware of your intelligence, both yours and Brother Zanna's. I appreciate it highly and think that tomorrow it will be of enormous value for the triumph of our holy mother the Church, and her Society. I certainly attempted to defend both of you in the outraged eyes of the father rector. I reminded him that the more richly endowed natures are those which are also slower to purify themselves. Now, however, it is essential that I forearm myself against other mishaps like those which have just occurred. It will be better for Brother Zanna to avoid your company for some time. Friendships can be dangerous, even if they are not special friendships, but merely intellectual friendships. From now on, in the groups which you form for the walk or for the periods of daily recreation, you will avoid the company of Brother Zanna. It is a small mortification which you will accept, I hope, in a spirit of gratitude.'

'Yes, father, I assure you I will.'

4

For some months, Andrea had no opportunity to exchange as much as a word with Brother Zanna. They saw each other continually, since almost all the exercises of religious life were conducted communally, but Brother Zanna seemed to pay no more heed to him. He appeared reserved and closed, a far cry from the man he had been during the early days of the novitiate. Andrea understood that it was hard, in there, not only to make friends but also to keep them.

The best friends were those acquired after facing a long period of adversity together, but the rotation and alternation of company to which everyone was subject made it almost impossible to face adversity in the company of the same person. 'There is no desert more to be feared,' thought Andrea, 'than a life without friends. Real friendship multiplies joys and divides problems.' And yet, some days, the suspicion grew that everything in their way of life was calculated to prevent the growth of a true, intimate friendship, or to set each one against the other. He could find no other way of justifying certain requirements laid down by the superiors, and he remembered having read that in the ancient monasteries of the primitive Church it had been common enough to see intimate friendships flourish under the benevolent eye of abbots and directors of conscience. One day, in the novitiate library, his eye fell on a friendly correspondence between two twelfth-century monks. He had noted with astonishment the tone of deep sentimentality which permeated those letters.

Intimate, friendly relationships were also bound up with the specific characteristics of the modern *devotio*. Perhaps the author of the *Imitation of Christ*, that prodigious little book which he had to read and meditate on each day, had in his own lifetime loved in a particular way some of his brothers, but that had not prevented him from writing the simplest and most profound book of piety in the world, a work rich in love of Christ. In his day, it was a normal and appreciated occupation for the beloved brothers of the community to observe one another closely, to spy on each other and exchange information on the movements of their spirit. Memories of Orestes and Pylades, of Damon and Pythias, of Theseus and Pirithous, not to mention biblical memories of David and Jonathan, held no fears for the monks.

Why, wondered Andrea, could not the same thing happen in his own time? Was it perhaps because at the roots of friendship, this feeling which not even love could replace (but was there really any difference between them?), there could no longer be found sincerity, fidelity or generosity, but only artificiality, sensuality and egoism? Andrea had always hated the indifferent glances exchanged between those who owed each other nothing; he had loved the gratifying and surprising affinities, the mute solidarity of hearts in search of each other. Now he was aware that he was engaged in a no quarter struggle on two fronts. First of all with God, and the problem was to establish who would wear himself out first. What was pleasing to the Lord, his superiors stated, was the blind hope of each of them in his mercy. Then there was the struggle with the others, with those whom Andrea believed he loved, such as Brother Lodovici. He knew that there should be nothing carnal in this affection, but when, in a friendship, there was no hint of the senses, he had the impression of

43

inhabiting emptiness and abstraction. It appeared to him terrible, well beyond his strength, to foster a spiritual love with no shadow of sensuousness. On the contrary, he thought that to love or to despise or merely not to love, often without any good reason, was all too easy for the human heart. The defects of one's neighbour leapt into view at exactly the right moment. The novice master never failed to warn him, in that good-humoured way of his, to imitate the bees 'who throw themselves on to the flower and steer clear of the thorns clustered around it': not to be like the cockroach, 'which goes straight for the dung'. As they were forced to live together the whole day in silence, words became really superfluous and clumsy instruments. A mere glance was sufficient to convey understanding. Besides, even during the periods of recreation when speech was permitted, neither the prearranged subjects of their conversations nor the conventions they were required to observe scrupulously among themselves served the purpose of bringing them together. They were obliged to speak stiffly and formally with each other, and that invariably ended up setting a false tone for the relationship, and creating a state of awkwardness among them. They were not even able to address each other by their Christian name, but only by their surname. Andrea knew that this, above all, clashed with the spirit of the early Society, when Ignatius of Loyola, wishing here too to distance himself from other religious Orders which were frozen in external forms and out of harmony with the times, established that only the Father General was to be called father, while all the others were to call each other simply by their Christian names, even if they were priests: the most illustrious and learned fathers were to have their names preceded only by 'master'.

*

One afternoon, during his walk, Andrea found himself alone with the brother named Lodovici, for whom he nursed a secret love. The novice who was to accompany them had been delayed at the last moment in the parlour for a family visit. Andrea said to himself that the long-awaited opportunity of finding himself face to face with Brother Lodovici had finally arrived.

It was an exhilarating winter's day, of sun, cloud and wind. They walked together up towards the lonely woods surrounding Lake Nemi. Quite abruptly, Andrea said that he felt tired and invited his companion to sit down on the high banks at the lakeside. Brother Lodovici searched for a clean spot on the withered, yellowing grass, sat down, pulled out an aged Bible with a battered leather cover and began to read aloud some verses of the ancient wisdom. He read to himself in a loud whisper, while Andrea gazed at his face, which seemed to him hungry for the eternal words. Andrea knew within himself that he would never forget that face, whatever happened thereafter: he may have forgotten many faces, but this face leaning over the pages of the little Bible would never fade from his memory. He saw printed on it all the immortal weariness of the world, together with the certainty of a victory which would also be immortal. There was in that haughty face tenderness, courtesy and a majestic severity. No matter whom it belonged to in reality, that face appeared to stand for a life of unflinching protest and struggle against the world and the flesh. For an instant, on account of that face, Andrea despaired of ever making himself understood by Brother Lodovici. The one thing of which he was certain was that that unknown man seated beside him had no more knowledge than anyone else of what happiness really was.

On the far side of the lake, huddled on the shore, the houses of Nemi could be made out, and beyond them stood some scattered and solitary villas, surrounded by white statues which appeared to awaken occasionally from their marble immobility and point into the wind . . .

Brother Lodovici pulled a branch from a tree and began to beat the air around him, all the while avoiding Andrea's stare. He had stopped reading. His soutane, which was too short for him, afforded a glimpse of his rough, black woollen socks, tucked inside a pair of badly worn shoes.

'Oh, Brother Lodovici,' Andrea burst out, 'if you only knew how happy I am to be here with you.'

He had spoken these words with such ardour, in tones of such sincerity, that the brother looked up at him in astonishment. Immediately that expression of surprise changed into an imperceptible frown. The young man had regained full control of himself. Andrea observed that Brother Lodovici's mouth was as straight and harsh as an open wound, his lips thin and tight, his chin hard and protruding, his forehead massive, while his large grey eyes were damp and attentive. The trees around them rose darkly above the skeleton-like branches of the rest of the woods.

'Don't get upset at my attitude,' continued Andrea, 'I wouldn't like to offend you in any way. I only want to show my friendship . . . Do you not believe, brother, in that mysterious affinity which might pair vice with vice and mediocrity with mediocrity, but which calls to the same hearth souls which have come down from the heights and are bound for a better destination?'

'Perhaps you are exaggerating, brother,' replied the other, lowering his eyes to the grass. 'I do not at all consider myself a soul descended from the heights. I am one of many, a mediocre being.'

Andrea thought that that young peasant, in his holy, enchanting boyishness, had no idea of how much he resembled those gentle, intrepid adolescents whom the Church had known in its earliest days.

'Do not hold yourself in such contempt,' he replied. 'Do you know what the brothers in the novitiate have nicknamed you? The Seraphic. You are the very image of innocence and mortification. You hardly ever raise your eyes from the ground. Oh, I do not believe that the elect in the condition they will assume after the resurrection from the dead will be much different from you.'

'You are exaggerating: you don't know what you are saying,' insisted Brother Lodovici, with a touch of irritation apparent in his voice. 'Believe me, brother, you upset me when you speak in this way.'

'Forgive me, but it is precisely because of your style of life that the brothers enjoy telling you things which are not exactly edifying, just to see you blush.'

'I know,' said Brother Lodovici, 'that some of you consider me a celestial simpleton. You think I must suffer the pains of hell when I mortify myself. But it's not true. I live in a state where everything contributes to making me happy in time and in eternity. I am in a condition where sin is rare, repentance readier and easier, and where everything – examples, advice, corrections – drives me towards what is good: a condition where, through prayer, the sacraments, silence and solitude, the soul keeps itself united to God and separated from the world. Is my condition not a privileged one? Why should it be a burden to me? I claim no merit for it because it is all so easy for me.'

Andrea had never heard him speak so much.

'The novitiate,' continued Brother Lodovici, 'is like a

47

Bethlehem for the novices, in other words, a *domus panis*, a house of bread, because here we take on board provisions for the voyage and for the great dangers we will surely meet. This, brother, is our August, these are the fertile years when we must set aside something for the years of famine and sterility, as St Joseph did.'

Andrea deliberately changed the subject, and brought up the question of the incompatibility or vanity of family feelings. 'God has created a kind of love,' he said, 'which is greater than the love of parents for their children, the love of men who love others independently of the ties of blood.'

Brother Lodovici interrupted him: 'I distrust these loves. Charity seems to me the only sort of disinterested love. As for us poor human creatures, even when we believe we no longer love a body but a soul, it is because this soul is enclosed in a covering of flesh, full of grace and gentleness. In reality, it is impossible to love a soul as one loves a body. It would be like loving a star. Charity is the only absolute, intense, perennial love in which the self is forgotten. The important thing, brother, is to know how to transform human attachment into spiritual affection.'

'Sometimes it simply cannot be done,' said Andrea quietly.

'We must distinguish,' continued Brother Lodovici, 'between love in its strict, essential sense, love which consists in wishing for and procuring the best for those we love, and its sensory, maybe even sensual, echo, in other words, the emotion produced by this love. If we are talking about the first element, the love of Our Lord can neither abolish nor diminish it. Indeed, the main effect of the love of Our Lord is to purify, widen, spiritualize this love, that is to say, to burn away its waste elements, its egotistical leftovers, its excessively carnal overtones. The love of God allows us to better order our affections, to make them purer without diminishing them, quite the contrary.'

They had risen to their feet and were walking towards Mount Pardo. The calm, grey countryside seemed to illuminate, reduce and heal their passions.

Brother Lodovici went on, 'But if the sensory repercussions of this affection come into competition or conflict with our love for Our Lord, everything becomes more difficult. Experience shows that this poor, miserable human heart of ours is completely overwhelmed by an affection which is too deeply felt. Love is free and is master of its experiences as well as of its gifts, but there is in its delights and inclinations a great deal of more or less conscious selfishness. The excess, the abuse of love, causes the heart to degenerate. They leave us weakened for the exercise of virtue or charity. They absorb us in the exclusivity, jealousy and sadness we permit ourselves, as well as in the satisfaction of self-love. When a person thinks of himself, he no longer loves. The principal obstacles to virtue in many souls are the disorderly movements of the heart, which these souls can no longer manage to regulate and moderate. An attachment to creatures is invariably something excessive and ruinous.'

'But this is the only attachment,' said Andrea, 'granted to certain natures . . . The other is too cruel, brother, it requires too high a level of inner renunciation, it involves a terrifying nakedness of heart.'

'This is the price we must pay at the beginning if the soul, formed in this way, is later, without any danger of self-love, to give itself generously to many. In any case, between the two extremes of absolute detachment from love and absolute freedom for its emotional repercussions on the soul, the degree will vary from individual to individual and, with time, for the individual himself. There are no fixed rules. But, brother, I do not believe that it is possible to exaggerate in the gift of oneself to Our Lord.'

They had reached the summit of Mount Pardo. The sea could be seen at the far side of the plain. The clouds had broken here and there into languid, golden wisps, affording a glimpse of the bright foamy waves as they broke against the dark rim of the shore. Andrea paused to look at the country-side. Its immobility and silence took on the heroic aspect of a tacit challenge to that vast sea in the distance, as silent and dark as despair. The two of them made their way down towards the sombre mass of the poor houses of Ariccia. Andrea no longer had any idea of what to say, but a single thought was beating in his mind, a thought which one day, almost by chance, he had heard formulated by Brother Zanna and which only now came back to him: 'The greatest charity is found in those who have broken the rules.'

5

During the vigil of fasting and abstinence which preceded the first Christmas Andrea spent away from his family and from the friends of his secular life, the novitiate was immersed in absolute silence for the entire day. This gave Andrea time to gather his thoughts and to reflect on the dregs of bitterness and desolation which filled his heart. He was going through a crisis whose principal external manifestation, a seemingly positive absorption in other people, was in fact an indirect confirmation of it. He threw himself so wholeheartedly into external practices and gave himself so generously to other people precisely because he wished to be as little as possible on his own, preferring to flee from himself for fear of recognizing in himself something which would drive him mad.

This crisis seemed to unleash all the moral forces, both sublime and perverse, from their deep prison and to raise his spirit to a sphere which he would, perhaps, have never attained otherwise. Andrea knew that, with his weekly confessions of boyish failings, he was not successful in re-acquiring purity of soul, and yet there never were any grave sins of which he could unburden his conscience; there never were, nor would there ever be, any concrete facts. If something genuinely blameworthy had occurred, he would have managed to free himself of guilt through confession, but it was difficult for him to accuse himself of turbulent emotions, of an impatience and restlessness of mind, of a see-saw of prohibited sensations, apparently unprovoked and always resisted, afflicting the flesh.

There were moments when not even faith seemed to offer him an understanding of the fundamental absurdities and contradictions of existence. The one reality which seemed to dominate him, with overwhelming cruelty, was the person of Brother Lodovici. That face of his had come to symbolize for him earthly beauty in all its dangerous mystery, a beauty whose transience in the midst of the incessant mortifications to which it was subjected, and whose pathetic insubstantiality in the environment in which it was wasting away, he could not fail to note. This reality, enclosed in itself, must not become for him a limit, the alpha and omega, his heaven and hell. Andrea attempted to react against it with all his strength. The time had come for his life no longer to be totally governed by emotions: time for him to learn to bear the yoke of religion willingly, not to attempt to shake off that yoke or diminish its weight; time for his soul no longer to have continual need of a stimulus to goad it, or of corrections to show it the straight path; time for him no longer to abandon himself to vain joys or allow himself to be beaten down by sadness. Andrea's concentration and resolution were of brief duration, and his conversation was often worldly. An unsuperficial observer would have been able to note that he was becoming ostentatious, bold and vengeful towards his environment. Even when he showed concern towards his brothers, he seemed to serve them with the punctilious precision of hatred rather than with the unruly alacrity of love. For some of the more ill-equipped novices, he had nothing but a veiled contempt. Others might imagine he was frivolous, but none could believe that in his heart Andrea lived for the one he loved and not for the world.

On certain days he felt as though he were suffocating in there, inside those big, grey, smooth, bare and impersonal walls. He yearned for the things that moved, the clouds on the hills or the waves in the sea. At those moments, he knew that he was still himself and had not in any way changed, as his superiors claimed or as the theory of grace itself suggested. He believed he was still totally the same boy who had always dreamed of some kind of personal immortality without ever managing to believe in it seriously.

At other times, a wild desire to escape from within those walls, to slip away into the world, to walk up and down as he had once done, and then to drink and listen to music with an inebriating sensation of physical liberty, would seize hold of him. That appallingly majestic building in which he lived, full of secret wardrobes and dark corridors where he was not permitted to linger, aroused a sense of nausea in him. 'A house like this has no purpose,' he said to himself on occasions. Then he would go out into the garden among the stocks, the spiraeas and the geraniums which grew in old terracotta vases or in ugly rusting pots. A terrifying sense of incompleteness weighed him down. He delighted in comparing himself to some lost young man filled with grace and courage. He called to mind all those fondly remembered dark old stories he knew so well. He looked towards the modest Mount Pardo, opposite, beyond the confines of the novitiate, as though looking towards an unattainable and alluring countryside blown by secret winds. Then, quite abruptly, he would go back into the house and, in an excess of fervour and energy, would mingle once more with the others, his presence creating around him a sense of vague popularity. The others felt themselves protected by his forceful presence, and did not know that he came to them in search of protection.

Even on Christmas Eve, Andrea thought long and hard about Brother Lodovici. He wondered what made him love him so much while he had not felt for even a single instant that his love was returned, or that there was any feeling in that cold, relentless being who made him suffer so deeply. Oh, without having seemingly done him any wrong, Brother Lodovici had always been as hard as granite. Why could he not sometimes be kind instead of always appearing so sensible? He, Andrea, would have been so good with the right person . . . Why could Brother Lodovici not be with him cheery, fresh and good-hearted, his eyes sparkling with interest and concern, as he had been for a very few fleeting moments? Why did he now seem so severe and hostile, the very image of someone who would spend his whole life agonizing over trivial things?

Andrea faced up to the long liturgical ceremonies of Christmas with stoicism. His inner turmoil became apparent in the great folds which all of a sudden appeared across his wide, pure forehead and in his keen, darting expression, always buzzing with busy thoughts. His body had stretched and seemed emaciated; it appeared that nothing could be more suitable as a refuge for a soul. In the choir, during the Christmas Eve functions, the young man found himself, quite suddenly, whispering to himself the litany of the Sacred Heart. When he got to the invocation *Cor Jesu, desiderium collium aeternorum*, big tears ran down his face, tears which flowed more readily the moment he realized they were being shed not for Christ but for a human creature who, imperturbably, a few metres from him, followed with compunction and measured fervour the phases of the liturgical ceremony. At that point he was seized by a kind of involuntary hilarity, the repercussion of the profound emotion he was experiencing. His laughter rang out above him for the briefest instant before being suffocated by the deep, grave notes of the organ inviting those present to join in the singing of the old hymns of hope. Immediately, he regained control of himself, and with only the slightest of delays his metallic baritone voice joined in with those of the choir.

One day, towards the end of the year, Andrea received a note from Brother Zanna. He found it between the pages of a book left lying on his table. It said: 'We have not been able to speak together for two months. I cannot stand it any more. This evening, I beg you, come to the library during meditation.' Initially, Andrea was terrified. He asked a senior brother with as much nonchalance as he could summon if it was permissible to write notes to others within the house without having them censored. The other brother replied that it could be done, since it was not a question of correspondence coming into or going out of the novitiate. That evening, Andrea made his way to the library while the other novices were deep in meditation in their rooms. He found Brother Zanna waiting for him. In a whisper, Zanna told him that they were not guilty of any grave misdeed since they were obeying a feeling of mutual charity, and charity stood above everything else, even above obedience. Unconvinced by these words, Andrea appeared frightened.

'Come on,' Brother Zanna told him, 'what are you worried about? The Jesuits are masters of mental reservation. Have you really learned nothing in the Society?'

'It is the first time,' replied Andrea, 'that I have the feeling, in here, that I am committing a serious error.'

'I could not live any longer,' murmured Brother Zanna, 'without exchanging at least a word with you, the only one who can understand me. With the other novices, it is impossible, and with the fathers, more than impossible.'

He appeared in despair. They stood face to face, hesitant

and embarrassed. Neither knew how to open the discussion.

'At times I am gripped by the temptation to leave,' continued Brother Zanna, 'but where could I go? Not back home: my people are poor, they work hard, they would not welcome me with open arms.'

'Speak to the novice master about it, brother, not to me,' interrupted Andrea apprehensively. 'What does it have to do with me? How can I help?'

'I will speak to the novice master when I have made up my mind.'

'But you must decide together. Otherwise, what is the point of having a spiritual director?'

Brother Zanna shrugged his shoulders. 'You know, brother,' he said, 'in recent days I have been thinking about Christianity and Communism. Basically, they resemble each other.'

Andrea's astonishment was so overwhelming that he had not the slightest idea of how to react, and stood listening with his eyes staring and his throat dry.

'Come on, don't put on that terrified face,' continued Brother Zanna. 'We are men in flesh and blood like the others, who reason and struggle. Where's the harm in this? We're not robots.' He smiled and went on, 'Communism is one of the many heresies of Christianity. It exalts human nature beyond every reasonable limit, and, like all doctrines which in their fanaticism claim to be able to improve man, it ends up debasing him, degrading him and making him a slave. Christianity, on the other hand, knows human nature better; it entertains no illusions about it. It weighs up the weaknesses and the inner frailty of man, and directs everything to the one end of correcting and overcoming nature by integrating and fortifying it supernaturally. However, sometimes it happens that even Christianity can suffocate human nature when it does not adopt the right means, or when it wants to make use of violent, authoritarian means.'

There was a pause. Andrea would have preferred to go, but it was no longer possible to leave. Zanna had started to talk once again, as though to himself. 'I have often asked myself, what is the task facing us believers in today's world, what must we do? And I have said to myself that we Christians must hurry to save man while there is still time. Tomorrow it will be too late, because he will refuse to be saved. He will have forgotten what he has been. The important thing, brother, is to adopt the right means, which are new means. I do not believe that priests, educated as they are today, are really much good. What do they know of life? What have they seen of the world? We, brother, came relatively late to the religious life, but what's to be done about those who, else-where, come into the seminaries as little more than children? They will never be able to understand the situations or the passions of people who live in today's world. They have no experience of the private problems which create havoc among worldly people, about their occasions of sin, of rebelliousness or indifference towards the Church, or, for that matter, of the forces which lie at the root of these difficulties.'

'But confession by people in the world,' replied Andrea, 'is a unique beacon of light on the passions which torment them, a penetrating study of the human heart, its instincts, its weaknesses and its victories. A young priest comes, in the course of a few years, to know more about the world than a thousand sociologists or psychologists, more than a thousand professional pedagogues . . .'

'Nevertheless,' said Brother Zanna, 'the priest does not have the direct knowledge of certain problems, at times the most important problems of everyday life.'

'This is true,' replied Andrea. 'The Church can give him only an abstract knowledge, even if it is complete and objective, of human vices and virtues. But it cannot be said that direct experience is invariably more valid than reflected experience. The Church is the depository of age-old human experience. Her wisdom is deep because it is the wisdom of the centuries.'

'This century, brother,' said Brother Zanna, 'will repudiate all other centuries and will either renew man or destroy him. This century has a thirst for a new, immense, more practical and fraternal wisdom, as well as for a more communal charity. The Church is making endless efforts to approach reality, a particular kind of reality which is pressing in on it, but she has managed only to make things worse both for herself and for this reality. In many matters, she is gambling boldly but not wisely.'

'What do you mean, brother?' asked Andrea.

'The Church has been infinitely more prudent and realistic in past centuries than today. It has repudiated the wise, moderate reforming zeal of its great centuries. The reforms which it has been implementing in recent times threaten to take her further away from humanity, instead of bringing her closer to it. Take one example: daily communion, which, as opposed to the tradition of all other centuries, the Church has wished to introduce, to recommend and even make obligatory in religious practice. Which of us, in here, would have the courage to decline it? And yet, daily communion imposes on us a terrible, inhuman tension if we wish to take it in the ancient spirit of faith and with the necessary purity, avoiding that indifference which normally results from habit. It is not allowed, under pain of committing a sacrilege, to be in a state of sin when we approach the royal banquet of Christ. Who can say what an enormous number of sacrileges has been committed since the day this practice was popularized in the Church? As recently as a century ago, communion was rare and sacrilege less frequent. It is true that everyone is allowed to abstain from the divine banquet, or is allowed to make a special confession, but how many, in the churches, seminaries and convents scattered all over the world, would dare to do so, either out of scruple or human respect? In here, in more than a year, I have never seen anyone refuse daily communion, or go to confession at any hour or day other than the standard Saturday hour, unless it was to interrupt that tired routine of habit and indifference with which these duties are normally carried out. With what very different fervour, brother, did the faithful in past centuries, on a few days in the year, approach the communion of Christ. Daily communion, as willed with such audacity and preached with such tenacity by the Church, presupposes a life lived on the highest spiritual plain, a life of absolute purity, a life of which not even the saints believed themselves worthy; after original sin, purity has not been prescribed for us as a prize but rather as a punishment. Only after undergoing punishment will we have a right to the prize.'

Their conversation was interrupted by the sound of foot-steps in the corridor. They separated in consternation, like two thieves about to be caught red-handed, promising to meet again soon. But this was not possible, because the period of holy quarantine had begun.

During the closing days of carnival, the novices undertook special meditations in reparation for sins committed in the world at that time. Andrea remembered other carnivals from his past life, and all the efforts he had made in those years to enjoy himself, and in a certain sense to proclaim his youth. On each occasion his enjoyment had a limit and quickly exhausted itself. In the world, only pain seemed to have no limits. Joy was varied, capricious and fitful. The sources of pain were, on the contrary, always monotonously identical.

With Lent, there began all the austerities of the religious life: the fasts, the penances, the endless rounds of self-mortification. Everything around Andrea was squalor and desolation and, in reaction, he found himself recalling more frequently the figures of his own past, all those whom he had loved and lost. Alone in his room, behind the screen, he pulled out some photographs which he kept in his table drawer and sat for a while with them in his hands, lulling himself with old memories. It had been such happiness, such happiness, and he loved them still and felt himself in turmoil when he saw those blessed faces in the snapshots they had given him. Oh, if only they would come and take him away for love of those bygone times . . .

Finally, he decided to hand the photographs over to the novice master, not without a hint of inner self-congratulation for that gesture of stoicism.

Within a few days, the month of spiritual exercises, during which they would not be permitted to speak, not even for a moment, not even during recreation, which was taken individually, would begin. Even outgoing and incoming correspondence would cease. All visits would be suspended. No one would be permitted to go out for any reason.

After Ash Wednesday, the beginning of Lent, the liturgy dropped the *Gloria* and the *Alleluia*, dressed the priests in violet vestments, stripped the deacons of the dalmatic and the subdeacons of the tunic, symbols of joy, and caused the organs to fall silent. The altars themselves were stripped; the images, with the exception of the cross, were covered with a veil. The novices followed an even more austere timetable: the time set aside for prayer was increased. This brought no consolation at all to Andrea, who was incapable of praying for long periods and who sometimes had the feeling that prayer was in vain, that it lost itself on desert paths or died in the vast silence of the heavens. He remembered that Ignatius of Loyola had once said that, of a hundred men at prayer, at least ninety-nine were deluding themselves – words which were permissible from a saint but which, if spoken by anyone else, would have aroused scandal and hypocritical protests. In his prayers, Andrea sometimes attempted to imagine God, to invest Him with attributes which he considered worthy of Him. If then something that he requested in prayer was not granted, he believed he had proof that petition-prayers did not reach their target. If the request was granted, he would search for physical causes which had produced that result. He was tempted to believe that it would have happened anyway, and so prayers granted became, like prayers ungranted, proof that all prayer was useless. He lacked the spirit of faith.

One freezing February afternoon, at precisely quarter to eight in the evening, the novices entered the grand silence. The spiritual exercises according to the method of St Ignatius of Loyola were beginning.

6

The decisive test, the trial of perseverance of spirit, was the long month consecrated to absolute silence and isolation. For the majority of novices, this month was the defining moment which often brought about a radical change in their view of life. Andrea understood that there were some books which he could not judge but which judged him: the book of the *Exercises* by Ignatius of Loyola was one of these. In a thirty-day dialogue with himself and with God, the novice was led little by little to that state of self-abnegation which made him capable of becoming a 'docile tool in the hands of the divine craftsman', in other words, a soldier of the Church Militant. The ideal of the *Exercises* was formulated in these four words: *Señalarse más en servicio. Más*, that is to say, 'more and more, ever more', was the most characteristic word of Ignatius's entire personality. From it, there derived two essential characteristics of his Society: obedience and discipline. The book of the *Exercises* offered a theology which, taking Creation as its starting point and passing through indifference to all human conditions, led to those things which 'guide better [*más*] to the end for which we have been created', specifically to the service of the Church in the Society. The *Exercises* existed, or did not exist, depending on whether or not their Christological foundation was upheld. Christ was not represented in the *Exercises* simply as a model to be imitated, an unchanging model chosen as such once and for all. He was presented rather as a living, working king who had not completed the mission of conquering the whole world entrusted to him by the Father. In order to achieve that, yesterday as today, He sought companions whom He could send into battle. Babylon faced Jerusalem. The duty of each individual was to make his own choice and then engage himself fully in the struggle. God, Church, Obedience: this was the Ignatian triad, this was the norm according to which the value of every moral act was judged.

Through an autonomous process of purification which subjected soul and body to a long, debilitating religious torture, the *Exercises* aimed to release the novices from all that was unrelated to the great ideals of obedience and discipline which they had vowed to follow in the name of their King, Church and Society. The tension to which the spirit of the young men was subjected assumed at times the character of cruelty: at the end, they were all worn out, they felt drained and, after thirty days of absolute silence, had nothing to say to each other.

Andrea reflected that, after such physical and moral suffering, a society and its intentions should be measured by the security they guaranteed in safeguarding all that was genuinely human in man. In this the Jesuits too, like every other human society, had often let themselves down.

He had learned to admire Ignatius of Loyola, one of the most hated and least popular saints in Christendom. His uncompromising brand of asceticism flew in the face of every form of traditional asceticism, whose aims had been the monastic ideal of *apatheia* and absolute spiritualization without regard for the body. Traditional ascetic doctrine had threatened, at a certain point, to attack the visible character of the humanity of Jesus and to destroy everything which was not pure spirit. Ignatius, on the other hand, had wished for a return to the Church visible, to its practical necessities and politics. In the very order of their spiritual practices, the Jesuits had contributed to the lessening in Christian life of the contemplative aspect and to the heightening of meditation pure and simple. Previously, it had been rather the senses and the imagination which had been set to work, but now the intellect and the will worked more.

The perfect Jesuit, according to St Ignatius, would always have 'antennae', would possess a refined sense of the demonic and the divine, not only in the contradictions of the inner life but even in the central occurrences of human history. He would also have a deep competence in all that concerned both Jerusalem and Babylon. Ignatius wanted his men to adopt, in the service of God, human means as though the entire outcome of the project depended on them alone, and at the same time to confide in God as though human means were of no worth. 'Virtue and holiness,' he repeatedly said, 'are splendid things in themselves and for themselves, but when contact is made with other human beings, unless prudence and ability are added, there will be something lacking in them and they will be insufficient in themselves.'

Jesuits were to struggle for the kingdom of the Church Militant. They were neither gnostics nor monophysites. They fought for Him who had been truly born, who had eaten and drunk, who had truly suffered under Pontius Pilate and had been truly crucified.

A whole new world opened out under the astonished eyes and excited senses of Andrea. He seemed able to penetrate Ignatian asceticism with an awestruck lucidity of mind. He meditated four times a day, each meditation lasting around one hour, and each time he appeared to find himself confronted with a new, more stimulating revelation. He was

helped in his meditation even by thoughts which were apparently unrelated to the essence of the meditation but which,
on the contrary, once analysed and mastered, vied with each
other to heighten the fervour and to deepen the topic of the
meditation. Andrea set himself the task of studying the life of
the founder of the Order to which he belonged. He read all
the biographies of the saint which he managed to find in the
library, and learned things which both astonished and excited
him. He reflected that Ignatius had belonged to a family that
reminded him, in many respects, of the Borgias. In his youth,
Ignatius had never disdained gambling, women or duels. One
of his brothers, a priest, had had four illegitimate children.
Ignatius himself, aged twenty-four, had been committed to
trial over a matter which remained shrouded in mystery but
certainly concerned his way of life, and had nothing to do
with the faith. It was only known that he had been accused of
'enormous crimes', probably unnameable excesses of some
sort. A drugged, overheated, heavy blood had flowed in the
veins of that sensual, violent *caballero*.

When the danger was great, God was none too fastidious
and chose his men from anywhere: Paul on the road to
Damascus; Augustine from the debaucheries of Carthage;
Francis from the wild revelries of the bohemian youth of
Umbria; Ignatius from among the smoking remains of a lost
battle. All of them had been called by mystical grace to
intervene at the most critical of moments. Against Hellenic
gnosticism and its mortal pride, God had brought forward
Ignatius of Antioch; against the neo-platonic and anti-
hierarchic mysticism which had infiltrated the Egyptian monastic ideal, he had brought forward two men – Basil in the
East and Benedict in the West, and had given both the task of
tempering monastic enthusiasm to the needs of the Church

visible. These moves had marked the end of spiritual anarchy, the renunciation of self-will, the return to perfect obedience as well as discretion in penitence and in personal asceticism.

The situation in the Church at the time when Ignatius of Loyola had begun his mission had been no less dramatic. Men in that era no longer knew what to think of the 'five plagues' of the Church visible. It seemed that a new, spiritual Church was on the march. 'We have had our fill of prophets, to the point of nausea!' exclaimed Bernardine of Siena. All the spiritual adventures of the age, from the Friends of God to the Brothers of the communal life, from the *devotio moderna* to the mysticism of Eckhart or of Gansfort, were imbued with the so-called cult of interiority and with pure, anti-ecclesiastical and anti-hierarchical spiritualism. The time which had preceded the Reformation had been a time of terrifying confusion. Only Catherine of Siena, that passionate devotee of the Church visible and of its Head, ever vigilant with her 'sweet prudence', and Bernardine of Siena, who juxtaposed the spiritual kingdom of Satan and the Church of Jesus (he had been nicknamed the 'Jesuit', a mysterious anticipation of the name which, one hundred years later, the members of the Ignatian Society would give themselves), only those two seemed to see clearly, and were thus deemed the most immediate spiritual precursors of the Spanish ex-hidalgo. It was incredible how divine omnipotence had transformed for its own ends that violent, unsavoury soldier into the master of modern apostolic practice and asceticism. The dissolute, swaggering ex-adventurer was the very same who now turned repeatedly, insistently, to God in a prayer taken from his mystical diary, a prayer which Andrea had learned by heart and repeated every morning: *Darme humilidad amorosa y así de reverencia y acutamiento.*

*

When, one afternoon in March, the month of exercises came to an end, the novices went down into the garden after the chanting of the *Te Deum*, and began to speak shyly. Their eyes were damp with emotion. The novice master had immediately joined them, bringing their correspondence.

Three of them were missing: two had had to give up the novitiate in exhaustion, while the third, Brother Lodovici, was lying ill in the infirmary. Brother Zanna, who had finally obtained permission to speak to him, came up to Andrea.

It was spring and on the far side of the plain the sea was sparkling. With his ink-black eyes, Brother Zanna seemed darker and leaner than ever. He looked like an old man. Andrea could not take his eyes off that tired, intelligent face. Everything on it except for the forehead, which had retained its freshness, seemed withered. He asked him if he felt exhausted after the exercises. Brother Zanna said no, adding that even if he was not in the first flush of youth, he did know how to make use of the Ignatian virtue of discretion. He smiled with something approaching malice.

'I am no longer young, like you,' he added.

'Oh, this is a defect which can be easily corrected with a good nap,' replied Andrea with a shrug of his shoulders.

They walked up and down a bit, slightly apart from the rest of the group. 'The final meditations of the *Exercises*,' said Brother Zanna, 'were the ones which gave me most satisfaction. They took as their subject the Passion of Jesus and his bitter struggle with the Pharisees, those puritans of Judaism. Basically, I am firmly convinced that, according to the teaching of Jesus, moral value does not come from external observance or integrity, but from the heart, from purity of soul, without which all the rest is vanity and hypocrisy. "The truth will set you free," He has said. Only his truth stripped of every other overlay will give us the freedom of children of God.'

He fell silent, waiting for Andrea to reply. Finally, Andrea said, 'From what I have been able to understand, the great law which informs the whole life of Jesus, especially at his Passion and death, is the law which gives us the explanation of all that He has done for us, the law which gives us the key to his earthly adventure, and that is the law of love. The world cannot give love because it does not possess love. The world is sodden with egoism; it is founded on everything that divides and dries up human hearts. The only really important thing for which we must thank God the Father is having revealed his Son to us. He so loved the world . . .'

Andrea interrupted himself because he saw the outlines of a smile on the thin lips of his brother, who was now beginning to mock him, to become fawning and unctuous. The Exercises did not seem to have transformed him in the slightest. All of a sudden, while the other was making his crass jokes, Andrea felt a kind of repulsion, which he immediately regretted.

As he moved off, Brother Zanna said only, 'Honey is not for a monkey's mouth.'

7

The day came when it was Andrea's turn to visit Brother Lodovici in the infirmary. Each evening, one novice had to drop by for around an hour to give a helping hand to the brother who was unwell. Andrea had awaited this moment with nervous impatience. He was still unaware of the nature of the illness which had afflicted Brother Lodovici. None of the superiors had made any reference to it in his presence, and when some of the novices had asked for information, they had been fobbed off with evasive replies.

This reticent silence exasperated Andrea, and one day, when he had been thinking at length about his sick friend, it drove him into a violent rage, causing him to break down in tears in his room.

No matter how many efforts he made to grope for a wider vision of things, for a wider horizon or a more penetrating light, everything there forced him to come to terms with the sacrifice of reason in an often incomprehensible servitude. He had to resign himself too to the coarsening of character brought about by a narrow, rigid rule which seemed to paralyse, through actions whose source was higher than nature, any development of energy. For him, the abnegation of the joys of the heart did not resolve itself in their fullness and sublimation. Certain nights he wept when he thought of that dry and barren trunk which was his life.

In the infirmary, he found Brother Lodovici, terrifyingly emaciated, lying on a white camp bed. When he saw him coming, the patient suddenly began to talk with an unsuspected level of vivacity. He said many complimentary things to Andrea, regarding his modesty, his intelligence, his various talents and on how the Society needed men like him. Andrea, somewhat surprised, waved the flattery aside. The other insisted. Then Andrea burst out, 'But I am deeply unhappy. You would be afraid, brother, if you knew who I am.'

Brother Lodovici appeared troubled by this unexpected confession, and immediately changed tack. He spoke without interruption, as though he were afraid silence might provoke some dangerous, unwelcome expressions from Andrea. Andrea was no longer listening to him but only gazing at him, and he thought he understood that the brother had by now guessed everything about him. Faced with that garrulous, gentle boy, Andrea was overwhelmed by a feeling of discouragement. All the negative elements of religious life suddenly crowded in on him: the distance from all that was dear to him, the dreariness of it all, the ugly, common things which surrounded him, the cloister, those long days of stifling narrowness, the mortifications imposed by the religious and communal life on individual tastes and aptitudes, the endless constraints of the rule. Brother Lodovici, on the contrary, stood for all that Andrea would have loved in the world, and which was forbidden to him by an obscure, cruel law. And, by irony of fate, it was precisely him, this same brother, who was the very incarnation in the novitiate of the austere, inflexible law which Andrea found so oppressive. He had nothing to offer in response to all this except a spirit of worldliness, of critical freedom, of half-heartedness, a spirit which deeply offended the one creature from whom Andrea particularly craved love. He felt sick at heart over the jealous wariness needed towards sensations, over the suppression of every joy of the senses and the slow suffocation of those faculties which required a certain abandonment to emotion, a certain *douceur de vivre* and a certain freedom of conduct. On some occasions, it seemed to him that his soul was failing in the face of so many mysteries. The renunciation of that liberty of action to which he had held so tenaciously in life now appeared to him an intolerable mutilation. He was still successful in mastering himself, but after each victory over the self, after each act of submission, he felt depressed. He was afraid. He recognized that he was incapable of the purity required by his vocation, purity of the heart rather than of the body.

Now he knew that Brother Lodovici also understood and, perhaps, felt all this, but the boy appeared entirely bereft of any feeling of pity for himself or for the weakness of others. Andrea loved and knew that he was loved in his turn, but there was no real reciprocity between the two affections: Andrea's love was not crystalline, while the love experienced by Brother Lodovici for him was made up of commiseration, virtue and charity. It was imbued with a sentiment unknown to Andrea, a sentiment which grew stronger the more it was successful in overcoming its own deep repugnance and invincible disgust for an interest extraneous to the spirit, an interest which brutally contaminated the person who was its involuntary object. Both, the one innocent and the other guilty, were in the midst of the flames, and had to be careful not to be consumed by them. Brother Lodovici was patient, humble and trusting. He knew that the transformation which required to be laboriously worked in Andrea would be a long, painful and difficult process. It would have to make of him, as of all of them, a celestial man, and that was terribly hard for young men of flesh and blood. Their life required them to divest themselves of all attachment for all that was lovable in the world. They were all under pressure.

At the end of the visit, the sick man asked the brother to pray for him.

'Oh, even if I wished not to,' said Andrea, shaking himself out of the torpor into which he had fallen, 'I could not stop myself praying for you, because you are the cause of constant distractions . . . I will pray all the time, brother, for your happiness and recovery . . .' Since Brother Lodovici was looking at him in surprise after that effusive outburst, he added, 'To pray for other people is a greater comfort to me than to pray for myself.'

'And I will spend much of my time praying for you. In that way, we will be equal,' replied the patient with a smile. 'But it is also necessary to pray for oneself.'

'Brother,' said Andrea, 'sometimes I find myself praying with horror, and the prayer seems to me, from a natural point of view, unreasonable and chimerical.'

Brother Lodovici's face darkened. 'No, do not say these wicked things. I promise that I will pray for you with great faith.'

'And I too,' said Andrea, 'when I pray for you.'

The sick man shook his head. 'Pray for everyone, and with the same spirit of faith. Promise me this.'

'When will we see each other again?' asked Andrea.

'Oh, I imagine, when your turn comes round again.'

'In about twenty days, then,' said Andrea. 'What a long time, brother!'

'It will pass quickly in prayer,' replied the patient.

That prayer they had promised to say for each other represented a soothing, invisible link which kept them together.

Even if it was hidden from the others, it was a cause of rejoicing for Andrea. Now his life was all the more easy to bear, even when it seemed beyond his strength, or against nature and simply impossible. He needed the courage to carry on to the end. The point was to try and be happy in a life like his.

Those twenty days were an eternity for him, even if all his prayers were addressed to God for the physical and spiritual salvation of the person he loved. Now he felt even more deeply the absence of Brother Lodovici, and the last days he felt as though he hated as never before in his life everything which caused separation, exile or forgetfulness. His old, worldly way of thinking about things began bit by bit to prevail once more, even within those walls. He struggled desperately against certain suggestions, but there always came a moment when faith appeared like a game of subjective illusions. The underlay of anarchism and subversiveness in his personality re-emerged and rose up against the evils and imperfections permitted by God, and even goaded him to judge his religious superiors, and despair of them. His vocation seemed to him a painful dream. He had no submissiveness, no humility of spirit. He could no longer take a benevolent view of the rules. He failed to put into practice that maxim which warned him to keep the rules and not allow himself to be kept by them.

In addition, it was useless for him to take resolutions, since he knew perfectly well that such resolutions would serve no purpose. And then, the old Adam continued to display diabolic skills. The real difficulty in attaining inner peace of mind or a sincere and unshakeable spirit of faith, derived from a dissipation of feeling and from an allegiance to the Church which, in the absence of any deeper union, was purely of the will. He was distracted too easily, and any item could trigger an automatic sequence of memories, each one triggering another. He could remain with his mouth closed for a whole day but real silence, inner silence, always eluded him.

When he was informed that it was his turn to visit Brother Lodovici the following day, he could scarcely contain his emotion. He raced into the garden on his own, even if that was contrary to the rules. He walked up and down the grassy, sun-drenched avenue flanking the hill. Beneath him, there stretched a plain of sleepy vineyards in full blossom. The sea in the distance was a foaming strip of gold and blue.

That evening, one of the novices assigned to him as companion during recreation said, almost casually, that Brother Lodovici had taken a turn for the worse. The brother infirmarian had let slip that the sick man was suffering from a tumour. That night, Andrea did not sleep. The following day, he found his brother in a cheerful mood. He seemed even thinner, a pitiful, bloodless thing on the little white bed of the infirmary. Andrea was aware of a sickly-sweet, slightly nauseating if scarcely perceptible smell filling the room.

'Why are you so sad, brother?' the sick man asked him after a few minutes of banal conversation. 'Is it because of me?'

Andrea found him changed: there was a lightness of spirit, almost a touch of irony, which he had never previously noticed. He told him he could not find inner silence. Brother Lodovici smiled.

'Oh, I understand you perfectly, you know. In an age of noise and clamour like ours, the silence imposed on us has something anachronistic, almost counter-productive about it.'

'On the other hand,' said Andrea, 'it facilitates intimacy with God.'

'For intimacy with God, the really important thing is to obtain detachment from the passions and from creatures. As long as there are secret gardens inside us, there can never be genuine intimacy with God. You do not have a secret garden, brother, do you?'

Andrea made no reply. It now seemed as though the roles had been reversed: the sick man teased Andrea about his feelings, while he remained silent, uncomfortable and almost resentful.

'Come on,' said Brother Lodovici, 'don't give us that expression, brother. It is me who is about to take my leave, not you . . .'

Andrea raised his eyes quickly on to the face that was smiling at him.

'Yes, look, I am reduced to a human rag, an object of disgust for those who are obliged to look after me. If you pull back the sheets, you'll see the sores which cover my back . . . and emit the evil stench, you know? And yet I am happy to give up all the so-called earthly delights.'

Andrea covered his face with his hands, and at the same moment became once more aware of the smell he had noticed previously, that horrible, subtle, sharp stench which tormented his nostrils and caught him at the throat, the mortal smell of a body in decomposition. That bed began to exercise a strange fascination on him, and he started to wonder why he was attracted by things that ground down the human soul, by weakness rather than strength, by defeats rather than triumphs of the will. Just a little while more and Brother Lodovici would no longer keep silence, but silence would keep him. That boy did not appear to have journeyed to the threshold of death in order to attest to the wickedness, the disloyalty and misery of the world. On the contrary, he was departing without regret, rancour or recrimination, as though life, real life, would begin for him beyond death. He did not even seem to pay heed to the faint noises which floated in through the window, to the muffled voices of the rippling, glittering stream of ambition, love, *joie de vivre*, illusion and all that represented the form and expression of youth at its most intense. He continued to wait patiently for the Lord to draw up alongside him and give him a sign.

Quite abruptly, Andrea remembered what he was supposed to be doing in that room. Then he went to great lengths to comfort the sick man and began to read him some pages of a spiritual book. When it was time to take his leave, Andrea rose to his feet.

'We will meet again,' he said, 'and we will continue to pray for each other . . .'

'Twenty days is a long time,' replied Brother Lodovici, 'but it is the custom of the Society to gather the whole community around the dying, if it is possible . . . One way or another, we shall see each other again.'

'Oh, brother, if you were to die, I would leave the Society, I would not be able to stand one more minute in here . . .'

Andrea never knew how these words managed to escape from his lips. There followed an oppressive silence. Finally, the sick man said, peacefully, 'If I were to remain alive and you, brother, could not manage to transform your love for me, then indeed you would have to leave . . . When I am no longer here, you will have every good reason for remaining and for dedicating yourself, without other obstacles, entirely to God.'

Then, for the first time, Andrea could imagine his future life in the Society without Brother Lodovici. The thought produced in him a sense of frustration, or perhaps the same horror of exile in a new world which must have afflicted man after the loss, through temptation, of paradise.

'What dangers could there possibly be,' he asked excitedly, 'in the love which binds me to you, brother? This love is like a shadow of what heaven must be. St Paulinus said that Christ is there between two beings joined in one spirit. There is nothing, or scarcely anything, worldly about my love for you. Why should I reproach myself for loving a simple and sincere soul who has never known in his heart the devil, the world or the flesh, except as something vague and foreign. Brother, I am aware of the suffering I cause you when I speak like this, but I beg God to bless you.'

Their words, their very conversation, only served to confirm the doubts afflicting the soul of the sick man, doubts which Andrea had been attempting in vain to disperse. Over that conversation, over that atmosphere, over both of them, there hung a dark shadow, the shadow of their own intellectual limits. Their moral value should be judged not according to the deeds, but only according to intentions. By focusing on what his love was not, Andrea ignored what it was, and ignored too his secret conviction that nobody could love Brother Lodovici more than him. He would have given his life for him, and no one could do more.

The sick man seemed to listen to Andrea with that patience which was not only a blend of moral courage and physical timidity, or simple constancy in the face of the rush of events and ease in bearing them, but also what the saints call 'patience in God', or, better, joy in tribulation. The features on Andrea's face seemed to cry out in harmony with the words, and there was in those words a strange magic. They sank into the mind of the sick man, one of the few totally convinced men left to the Church. Compared to him, Andrea felt himself a newcomer to goodness, but it occurred to him that sometimes the latest arrivals could see further than the others. Against the obstinacy of the sick man who seemed to refuse to understand him, he continued to talk and defend himself, even if he already suspected in his heart that the God who moved the world would not have wished, nor would He have been able, to change His plans for his advantage or to do anything for him. He was not aware that he was behaving like a man who, in spite of being in possession of a religion, had no belief in the supernatural. He did not know that the other was struggling inside himself not to judge him as corruption's slave, one of those who, having once fled the impurity of the world, stumbled back into it and allowed themselves to be newly overwhelmed by it. Brother Lodovici saw that Andrea's eyes were bereft both of worldly and of religious faith.

'Marco,' said Andrea hoarsely, 'can you forgive me?'

The sick man stuttered, 'I think I should be asking pardon of you, brother.'

'Why?'

'For having sown confusion in your mind by my mere presence, even if I did nothing to provoke such disorder. Brother, I beg you, be yourself once more. How have you got yourself into this situation?'

Andrea retreated slowly towards the door. He stopped with his back to the wall. 'Marco,' he said in a whisper, 'forgive me, forget the formalities and the rules and all the rest just for one moment . . . as though there were only the two of us in the world . . . Oh, do something so that when I lose you, I do not lose everything . . . everything that is sweet and kind in this world . . . You, Marco, have the best of me, with nothing of me that is vile.'

He broke down in sobs and would have kissed him to stop him replying at that moment, but from the miserable iron bed, there came no reply.

'Tell me, Marco, do you believe we will meet again? I so much long to see you one more time.' Since he received no reply, Andrea left the room.

In the following days, the thin, sickly, nauseating smell which Andrea had noticed in the sick room filled first the infirmary, then the rooms nearby, before drifting along the corridors, spreading out and penetrating the entire house.

Hour by hour, the brother infirmarian sprinkled and sprayed perfumes throughout the rooms and corridors, but the mixture of scents did not help lessen the sharp stench from the infirmary or reduce that fetid smell, horrifyingly natural and more tenacious than any mere man-made perfume, of human flesh slowly decomposing.

A further thirteen days went by. The novices took their turn every night at the bedside of the dying man. They later told each other how they spent an hour in a terrifying stench which made breathing impossible, beside an unrecognizable creature who was decaying bit by bit, who had an immense cavity situated beneath the skeleton of a chest, in the place where the stomach should have been. The flesh came away in strips from the joints, the sheets had to be changed hourly. Not a groan, not a word came from the mouth which opened and closed spasmodically, while the glassy, dilated eyes remained open, allowing a glimpse of consciousness somewhere behind the pupils.

One morning at five o'clock, the novices were hurriedly awakened and conducted to the sacristy. Together with the priests, they donned the liturgical vestments, a candle was stuck in their hands and then, in procession, they moved to the infirmary, to be assembled in the room next to where their colleague lay dying. There they recited in chorus the prayers for the dying. Their brother's death-rattle could be heard. The father rector, the novice master and the brother infirmarian had entered the room where he was lying.

Nearly an hour later, Brother Lodovici passed away. The community dispersed and resumed their routine practices. Only later in the morning were the novices permitted to go and see the remains of their brother, laid out in the black robes of the Society. Beside the corpse, they found two men, the father and one of the brothers of the dead man, with a subdued and embarrassed appearance.

Andrea did not shed a tear when he knelt in front of the corpse, which was laid out in a humble, uncovered coffin. The stench which had emanated from that body in the last days of his life had now lost its violence and had settled to a dry smell of dust and ageing. Those unfamiliar remains seemed not to have known, for the whole period of their cold, earthly autonomy, the secret struggles of the soul. Andrea attempted to pray for what remained of Marco's passion for men, for the world and for God. Then he went to take refuge in the library, while all around him the agitated brothers busied themselves with their work.

The two days which followed were for him filled with confusion, with insomnia and with strange appetites. One night he remained alone for a few moments watching over Marco, who was now closed in the wooden coffin. He had taken a Bible with him. In a loud voice, in the profound silence of the night, he recited some verses of the twenty-third Psalm: 'The Lord is my shepherd. I shall not want. He maketh me to lie down in green pastures: he leadeth me beside the still waters. He restoreth my soul: he leadeth me in the paths of righteousness . . .'

The morning of the funeral was full of bustle. The coffin

was carried out of the cloister towards the dead man's relatives, who were waiting in front of the novitiate house. The sun was shining and Andrea observed the pleasure people took in breaking the monotony of their days, even for sad occurrences such as this. The superiors stood silent and glacial. Andrea, looking at them, managed to contain his distress for a moment.

And then everything was rapidly over. They placed the coffin on a hearse, and the funeral procession moved silently towards the small cemetery on a nearby hill. The group went on foot behind the vehicle, stopped in front of a gaping hole in the ground until the coffin was lowered, swaying as it went, and earth was thrown over it. A wooden cross was placed above the tomb and his name, nothing else, was carved into a rough stone.

They returned in silence, without tears. The only person who remained beside the tomb was the gravedigger, a sturdy young man who began to bite greedily into a sandwich. It occurred to Andrea that this was a slightly obscene symbol of life.

8

Quite suddenly, a warm, rainy week, the supreme delight of summer, arrived. Now the novices were able to savour life in the open air, their boundaries being the little woods of holm oak and pine trees, beyond which the life of their times went on at its own obsessive pace. In the late afternoon, they would stroll around the house. Ivy grew in untidy clumps here and there in the rockery, and the bushes rustled gently. The peal of the bells took on a life of its own in the fading light, and they would often stop to listen, glad of any interruption to their own dull conversations. At night-time, in the crisp air, a riot of seeds and buds, a flow of sap and lymphs and a surge of spring water would seem to split the earth apart. The skies were cloudless and ashen-grey and bright with starlight and lit by flashes of real or apparent lightning. Sometimes a huge, misty moon rose over the countryside.

Andrea often saw Brother Zanna sitting alone on a garden bench, making no gesture, seemingly thinking no thought, until one of the novices aroused him. On other occasions he appeared restless, as though devoured by some uncontrollable inner unease. One evening, Andrea found himself by chance in his company as one of three novices thrown together for the recreation period. After a few moments, the third brother was called for a meeting with the father rector. The two remained alone.

'For some time,' said Andrea, 'something has been upsetting you, brother.'

Brother Zanna appeared pleased to be finally given the opportunity to unburden himself. 'The superiors too,' he replied, 'are of the opinion that I'm not getting on well in here.'

'Why not?' asked Andrea.

'It seems that I have no love for obedience.'

'Obedience is something proud and gentle.'

'Words, words, mere words, brother,' cut in Brother Zanna. 'Words which have nothing to do with the kind of obedience required by the Society.'

Andrea waited for him to explain himself.

'Obedience,' continued the other, 'should make everything lighter, but it weighs on me like a curse.'

'The obedience which is required of us,' said Andrea, 'is voluntary; it is an inner holocaust of the will, an obedience for which we freely sacrifice that gift which is physical freedom. By choosing to be Jesuits, we have signed a blank cheque.'

Brother Zanna did not appear convinced. 'Who cares about the sacrifice of physical freedom? We ourselves willed it. The question is more to do with preserving inner liberty, the liberty of spirit and conscience. Not liberty in an absolute sense, of course: there is nothing absolute, excepting God alone. Nevertheless, I doubt if this liberty of the spirit can really be safeguarded by the renunciation of the free use of our intellect which we are compelled to make. We must strip ourselves of all those irrational elements (feelings, prejudices, habits, tastes, likings) which are often the life of the intellect, even if they do obstruct its pure activity. Can blind obedience of the sort demanded by the Society ever be intelligent obedience in the interpretation, execution, completion, anticipation and, if necessary, replacement of a command? Can blind obedience ever be anything other than servile obedience? To what extent can it be born of a spirit of love and to what extent is it the product of some maladjustment caused by fear or undue respect for our fellows? Is not the personality of the individual irremediably compromised by it?'

Andrea, from his poor, human point of view, felt that he was right and yet, in the teeth of his own deeply held convictions, he struggled to rescue that soul from the doubts which were tormenting it.

'Are you not forgetting, brother,' he said, 'that there exists a subtle distinction between personality and personalism, that is to say, the hyperbole or caricature of personality, when natural gifts, whether disguised or clashing with one another, serve only to satisfy man's natural egocentricity. Personality, on the contrary, is strengthened by obedience, which unerringly and unremittingly directs all the talents of the individual towards the one purpose. The best proof of this lies in the fact that the Society has produced from inside itself, thanks to or in spite of obedience, personalities who were gigantic and heroic not only in sanctity but also in the will, in the heart, in doctrine.'

Andrea's words made Brother Zanna think long and hard. Finally, he raised his head, which he had kept bowed for some moments. He replied, 'It still seems to me that no other human society, except perhaps a Marxist society, is more totalitarian than the Society of St Ignatius. In it the individual is nothing and the organization is everything. Everything in the Society is established for the sake of the Society and is hostile to the individual. In submitting individual interest to the common interest, the Jesuits have anticipated by centuries today's social doctrines, not to speak of all those theories of the subordination of the individual to the state and society, be it capitalist or communist.'

'There is something in what you say, brother,' replied Andrea. 'On the other hand, you must admit that our iron spirit of obedience has, when you get down to it, nothing at all in common with the climate you'll find in military bodies, or in some police states or dictatorships, where obedience rests not on the voluntary and free submission of the mind, but on the most brutal repression. It is only right and proper that in our days various forms of collective or social apostolate, built on a strict spirit of obedience, have taken over from the more antiquated forms of individual apostolate, which, however admirable and beneficial they may once have been, have shown themselves less effective and responsive to the urgent requirements of our age. This is why, today more than ever, in the Society's novitiates where young recruits are trained, every form of individualism is looked at askance. Any type of distinctiveness will be resisted as a grave evil.'

'Oh, I don't know,' said Brother Zanna, 'if I'll be able to give up mine.'

They fell silent for a few moments. Andrea continued, 'To those of us who have chosen the religious life, physical liberty is denied, but so is moral liberty when it goes beyond certain moral limits whose unchallengeable guardian is the conscience of each individual.'

'For a real Jesuit, this is blasphemy,' interrupted Brother Zanna. 'In the Society, there exists only a collective conscience, an institutional conscience. There is no place for the individual conscience . . . but if, on the other hand, the human conscience was created free, why are our individual consciences so repressed in here? We have given up both liberties, physical as well as moral. We have pawned our consciences to the Society for the whole of our lives.'

'Physically, man can turn where he wishes,' said Andrea,

'but, morally, his will is bound by the duty to do good and spurn evil, in deference to a transcendental law of which the Church, and the Society on her behalf, is the trustee. False liberty is founded on the total autonomy of man, and confuses physical liberty with moral liberty. If we have freely given up physical liberty, the only liberty truly permitted to us, why should we not also surrender moral freedom, which is only apparent, inasmuch as it can never ignore divine law? If we consider ourselves true sons of the true Church, this surrender should·not cost us too dear . . . If in addition we have chosen to serve God in the Society, where the holocaust is even more complete and demanding, we should be exultant, we should rejoice, brother, in this mortification which surpasses all others.'

'The Church, the Society and the superiors stand between the divine law and my conscience,' replied Brother Zanna. 'There are too many instruments which obstruct and suffocate the free, spontaneous dialogue between the Christian conscience and its God.'

At that moment, another novice came up beside them, so they were compelled to change subject.

Later, thinking back to that conversation, Andrea was appalled at the words he had spoken. He was beginning to say things which had a fine ring from a Jesuit novice, but which did not correspond in any way to what the man within was thinking. If he had been sincere, he would have had to recognize that he, as much as Brother Zanna, did not seem to have entered fully into the truth of his vocation. He did not realize that the Lord's pleasure, and his will, as transmitted by his authorized interpreters (the rule and superiors) were in no way meant to seem so dismal to him. In addition, it was galling to hear it repeated all around him that human links were to be transformed into spiritual affections. He could not see the possibility of such switches as long as there were certain faces, glances, voices . . . He was free to commit himself to this path, as he repeated constantly to himself, but if he were to commit himself, he would have to embrace the cruel sacrifices it required. The experience with Brother Lodovici had been of some value. His friendship for him had been different and deeper than the friendship he felt for other members of the community, such as Brother Zanna. It had not been licit if it had removed part of the charity he owed the others.

He could see now that there had been nothing wrong with that affection: what was forbidden were the sensual overtones, and the feelings which accompanied this affection.

He was rescued from his recurrent memories of Brother Lodovici and from the anxieties which Brother Zanna aroused in him by the practice of the so-called 'lowly and humble offices', which, following the first, fundamental and most important trial of the spiritual exercises, each novice in turn was required to carry out.

Now he found himself working all day long in the storeroom, washing dishes and pans, looking after the pigs in the courtyard, peeling potatoes, sweeping floors and attending to the bees in the hives. From time to time, while at work, his eyes met those of Brother Zanna peering at him with ironic curiosity from a distance. Zanna's behaviour revealed a sort of haughty, worldly impatience which irritated Andrea, even if he attempted to control himself in the knowledge that he was prone to allow himself to be overwhelmed by first impressions. Brother Zanna's intolerance and unease with the environment he inhabited were becoming more and more obvious. He was gloomy, continually absorbed in thoughts which Andrea imagined he knew but whose violence and intensity were quite beyond him. The other young man gave the impression of being at every moment prey to an impatience which was more than physical, which clouded his mind and weakened his will. Andrea, on the other hand, was beginning to appreciate the virtue of patience, to become aware that it offered enlightenment and afforded him time to form a balanced judgement of things and to seek corroboration. Impatience, on the contrary, sprang from a narrow view of reality through the prism of one's own ego.

During the interviews with the novice master, Andrea felt that he had got over the suffering he had felt at an earlier stage, when each shortcoming which was brought to his attention provoked in him minor inner explosions of resentment and anger. Now he could listen with a tranquillity bordering on indifference to the voice of his superior as he listed his defects, reproaching him for being too impulsive in speech and act; for abandoning himself too frequently to the spirit of criticism towards his colleagues; for the untidiness of his desk; for occasionally lacking in gravitas by running or humming; for being too categorical in his judgements and for not treating the entire confraternity with even-handedness.

The novice master showed himself absolutely intransigent on questions of good manners, which he considered a form of charity. The rules of modesty had to be observed rigorously from the very first days of religious life. They even laid down, with that love for detail which was typical of the spirit of the Society, the normal expression of face of the perfect Jesuit. The head, for example, was to be kept ever so slightly bent forward; the lips were not to be kept unduly apart; the furrowed forehead should be avoided, and the nose should never be turned up. Of special importance was the custody of the tongue: it was absolutely forbidden to use 'indecent, strong, arrogant, wounding, vain, futile, flattering, mendacious, demeaning' words. There was a special notebook set apart for everyone to list shortcomings in this respect. The novices were required to appear serene and impassive on every occasion. Even when suffering, they were required to dissemble. The aim was to deepen as far as possible that disinterested, perhaps heroic, cruelty which each was expected to employ as a further gesture of self-torture.

In time, Andrea even learned that art of conversation which, because it was intermittent and recreational, was specific to the religious life. It consisted in talking artlessly, with fluency and simplicity, accommodating to the character and inclinations of the people with whom one was conversing, sticking to the point and avoiding any too obvious form of rhetoric or eloquence. He learned to avoid paradoxes which had no value except for spirits bereft of all sense of measure and, in consequence, of prudence. The school of the Society also taught them never to complain, since complaints invariably provoked in other people, particularly among the numerous enemies of the Order, the desire to insult rather than compassion or pity. 'Those who complain of wrongs endured in the past,' according to the novice master, 'leave the way open for future wrongs and draw nothing but contempt.' The prudent man, on the contrary, should never talk in public about his own defects, but only about those things which served to arouse the esteem of friends and to keep enemies in their place.

They should never be too familiar with strangers, since a heart without secrets was an open letter. Reserve should be a natural consequence of the control they exercised over themselves. Even truth required considerable circumspection, since it took as much ability to speak truth as to keep it secret. 'Not all truths can be voiced,' warned the novice master, 'some because they are of great importance to us alone, others because they are of great importance to others.' It was also better not to form such a high opinion of people as to be intimidated in their presence. No one ever trespassed beyond the narrow limits accorded to humanity. The dignity of rank and office conferred an apparent authority which rarely corresponded to genuine merit. Imagination was prone to race ahead and imbue things with a grandeur they did not possess; it perceived not only what was there but also what could have been there. It was as inappropriate for ignorance to be bold and impertinent as for ability to be timid. If self-confidence was of great value to those who had no brain, all the more was it useful to those who had great brains.

Another recommendation offered by the priests was to acquire deep knowledge of one's own predominant defect. It was essential to wage open, relentless war on it. To unmask it was to defeat it, particularly if the person in thrall to it considered it as dangerous as it appeared in the eyes of other people. If they were successful in uprooting their principal imperfections, they would find it easier to grapple with all the others.

'Enter with what is theirs, exit with what is ours' – this was the precept which, hammered home time after time, had made the Society great. To enter, in other words, in the guise of serving other people's interests, to come away with what was in one's own interest. No stratagem had ever been more suitable for obtaining what was desired. The directors of conscience themselves recommended this holy snare for everything connected with eternal salvation.

*

Andrea's greatest difficulty lay in being required to be simultaneously active (and therefore sure of himself and of his actions) and docile (and therefore in a state of total spiritual dependence), in allowing his every action to be controlled by authorities whose thinking was often beyond him. He felt there was an imbalance between this rigidly artificial style of life, this climate of perpetual inner crisis, this austere institution which framed the religious life, and the men who were compelled (by vows or by their fidelity to their own vocation) to live inside it. As with every other young Jesuit, the anxious conviction gnawed away at him that if the world was changing with such frantic rapidity, it was no longer sufficient merely to adapt to new circumstances. The point was to take the initiative, as Brother Zanna so heatedly maintained, and direct the new circumstances from which a new age would emerge. The painstaking, prudent purpose of carrying out his routine duties and observing the ordinary rules was no longer adequate. For those young men who now wore the robes, 'with unprecedented offhandedness' (as the novice master had once put it), the currents of modern thought were not only irreversible but also incomprehensible within the parameters of the traditional, antiquated schemas where the elders preferred to see them enclosed.

Among the novices, Brother Zanna provided the most alarming example of this state of intolerance. His attitudes were all the time becoming more undisciplined and rebellious. He made an open display of his discontent and was deaf to the appeals of his superiors. He gave the impression of merely going through the motions with his every act, even the most trivial, and succeeded only in irritating those in the community who, like Andrea, felt closest to him. The young man took delight in showing himself to be distinctive, even extravagantly so. He no longer had any idea of how to overcome his own spiritual isolation.

One day, during the period of recreation, Andrea met Brother Zanna with a bunch of flowers in his hand. He laughed when he saw him. He appeared odd with those flowers, and Andrea said so.

Brother Zanna replied, 'You forget that the greatest painter of flowers who ever lived was a Jesuit, Father Seghers.'

'Yes,' said Andrea, 'but you, brother, are making yourself stand out, and that is viewed none too kindly in here.'

'Do you really believe that I get up every morning at six o'clock to agree with everyone else?'

There was a touch of scorn in his voice. Andrea decided he could no longer love him. He was too sarcastic, too embittered and too unjust: he had converted himself into a creature of prickly resentment. In addition, it did not seem possible to Andrea to continue loving people with whom one was compelled to live from morning to night as a matter of routine. And he wondered if those whom he had really loved in life had not been, perhaps, strangers whom he had met for a few fleeting seconds, whom he had desired and longed for in dreams, or who had passed close by him, had exchanged a glance with him before going out of his life for ever.

At the end of July, the novices all moved into the mountains, in Abruzzo, for a month's holiday. They arrived one evening at Campo di Giove, a tiny village nestling at the foot of Mount Maiella, about a thousand metres above sea level, where the Society owned an old country villa.

Andrea passed a month there in the open air, away from the irritations of discipline, feeling freer now that he was required to undertake nothing more exhausting than excursions and picnics in the countryside. The periods of recreation were more frequent and the novices enjoyed greater freedom of speech. The only one who took excessive advantage of this was Brother Zanna, who had now no scruples and no longer made any attempt to dissemble or conceal that cool, calm, intellectual pride which left him more and more estranged from the rest of the confraternity.

During an excursion organized for the entire community, Andrea decided to put him on guard against the negative reputation he was acquiring. The two of them had moved away a little from the rest of the group.

'It's time to face up to it, brother,' said Andrea. 'There's a gulf between your endless challenges to the community to which you belong and the attitudes which are normally associated with the perfect Jesuit.'

Brother Zanna burst out in scornful laughter. 'The apparently humble and submissive attitude you find in all fully formed Jesuits has nothing to do with any deep feeling of humility or desire for mortification; it comes from a secret yearning, never satisfied, to win the love of their neighbour. There's something atavistic about it, something in the blood.'

'I don't understand you.'

'The Jesuits have never felt themselves loved, either inside or outside the Church.'

Andrea replied, 'There is nothing strange about this Order being an object of hatred for the enemies of the Church.'

'But it would be an idea, wouldn't it, to try and find a foundation, should we say a theological foundation, for that instinctive aversion shown towards us even inside the Church,' replied Brother Zanna. 'You might even detect somewhere some legacy of the Order, passed down from the first days of its existence. Centuries ago Suarez noted these feelings of antipathy in the ecclesiastical circles of his time, feelings which took the form of reproaches for displays of arrogance, for the mania for new methods, for indifference to tradition. There are undoubtedly many human idiocies behind these complaints, but if you go to the root of things, you will find the cause of this opposition in the very nature of the Society of Jesus. What upsets people about the Order is its limitlessness, the fact that it recognizes no standard apart from the day-by-day struggle inside the Church for the conquest of souls by any possible means for the visible kingdom of God: it is this willingness to be involved on every front, irrespective of peaceful forms or of boundaries between different tasks. In certain ecclesiastical circles, today as much as yesterday, it is impossible not to be aware of a vague impression of threat in the face of this *sollicitudo omnium ecclesiarum* Jesuits attribute to themselves, of this constant possibility of change of tactics, of underhand meddling, or of some new drive. There is something significant in the accusation made against them of seeking to express by the very choice of name (a name which, properly speaking, is the appropriate name for the entire Church) the fact that they feel themselves called to preside over the destiny of this whole body.'

Once again, Andrea recognized that Brother Zanna's analysis was not lacking in insight, but at the same time he felt it his duty to set other considerations, of no lesser validity, against the novice's arguments. He feared that Brother Zanna too might one day abandon him, leaving him all alone, in there.

'The Society, brother,' he said, 'must keep faith with the fundamental justification for its vocation, and must persist, in good times and bad, in its mission of keeping alive inside the Church that restlessness which is the source of life and without which it is impossible to move forward the kingdom of Christ. In this unending war which the Society is conducting, final triumph is assured, even if some phases of the struggle will not necessarily be victorious.'

Their conversation was once again interrupted by other novices who drew up alongside them. Andrea understood, by merely looking Brother Zanna in the face, that he had not managed to convince him.

While other members of the community moved happily backwards and forwards around him, he felt a great sadness weigh on his heart: a sadness which changed to discouragement when, on the way back, he met two men who lived in those mountains and watched them put their hands on their testicles when they saw the group. That gesture of contempt and spite, petty and instinctive as it was, no less demeaning for those who did it than for those who were its involuntary cause, seemed to spring from an ancestral fear or from some immemorial superstition. Andrea, dogged as he was by obsessions which had long troubled him, could not get that gesture out of his mind.

9

In early September, they returned to Galloro. Andrea's first year in the novitiate was drawing to a close, and with it the minimum time laid down by canon law prior to taking the vows. Now he knew that his conversion had been a point of departure, not of arrival, and would in all probability remain such for the entire duration of his religious life. It was this that Brother Zanna, with his ambition to resolve and reconcile during his novitiate all the problems and contradictions which surfaced in his mind and heart, seemed unable to grasp. Conversion was by no means a process of sudden death and rebirth as something different. Every conversion was simply the result of following a sign which pointed, in the midst of a thousand difficulties and doubts, in a new direction, and which, between a thousand reversals and delays and regrets and lapses, organized the whole inner world according to a new scheme. Unfortunately, their life was not one integrated whole made up of the special content of their mind, and of the fabric of their loves and dreams.

Andrea's wish was to reach the unique, authentic reality of being, the reality of the supernatural. He had not succeeded, and indeed felt himself incapable of the effort. The old things had not disappeared and came searching for him, even in there, and he did not believe that he would ever be left in peace. Nevertheless, this was not a reason for him to feel, like Brother Zanna, that he had been defrauded, cheated or prevented from dedicating his existence to God. Basically,

Andrea suffered more from the tiny material inconveniences of the monastic life than from the one great human sacrifice it demanded. He suffered, for example, from the lack of books. During the novitiate, their reading was restricted to spiritual books. Later on, during the long years of academic education, the Order would aim to build in each individual a solid intellectual base of sufficient breadth to permit the establishment of a philosophy of life and faith, an absolute necessity for spirits irresistibly spurred on by currents of modern thought to doubt and question everything.

In that reclusive life he had freely chosen, Andrea found himself educated day by day in the school of suffering, but here, as elsewhere in today's world, if man suffered greatly, it had also to be said that he suffered badly. There was in contemporary suffering a sickly element which crushed all forms of energy. A crisis of the will, a paralysis of the combative and recuperative faculties produced suffering without struggle. This explained, among other things, the fearful vacuum encountered in seminaries, and the large numbers of men who, after joining the novitiate, gave up a little way down the road they had chosen and had initially travelled with such enthusiasm and sincere dedication. There had never been so many wandering eyes as in these times, ran the lament of the superiors. 'The wandering eye dissipates the spirit,' according to the novice master, 'and exposes boredom and the absence of thought.' On the other hand, all too frequently an eighteen-year-old boy, newly arrived from the country, was asked to display a maturity which could not be other than a fiction or a mask, because it did not have its origins in age, character or the circumstances of life. Could it ever be possible for a boy emerging uncertainly from puberty to appreciate how beautiful and sad it was, but how strong he had to be, to begin to understand the emptiness of human things and to open the ears to the relentless rush of eternity? And what about those tender, special friendships to which he would be violently and unavoidably inclined as a result of a cloistered, strictly all-male life, but which he was obliged to resist with all his strength under pain of serious censure? The young men who struggled, with themselves above all, and who were thrown together in there, grew up as closed, passionate, obstinate and wilful creatures. They nurtured a naive hatred of their own body as though it were a ferocious enemy. Friendships exploded among them with that character of brusque violence which people in the world outside recognized happily as the first symptoms of love. But then what? Then there was for them nothing but a long, debilitating struggle under the eyes of a hostile, distrustful community to suffocate, forget and destroy that friendship.

Personal opinions were not permitted. A novice was not allowed to hold opinions. If in the world outside judgements were made according to the good and evil people were capable of doing to each other, novices were not permitted to judge anyone or anything. Everything had to be accepted, and where possible understood, in the most absolute silence, that silence against which Brother Zanna, heedless of the disciplinary sanctions which were his lot after every infringement of the rule, rebelled with growing frequency. On one occasion, when Andrea had gently reproached him for this defect, he had replied aggressively, 'Brother, which silence are you talking about? That rare, supernatural silence known to the mystics? Or this silence of ours, so similar to the silence Luther considered a curse?'

On that occasion, the young man had opened his heart fully to Andrea. They were alone in the garden, plucking ripe fruit.

And once more Andrea had the impression that it was his own conscience, stripped despairingly bare, which was talking through the mouth of Brother Zanna.

'I am tired,' Brother Zanna had said. 'I do not have the strength to make the decision myself, but sooner or later the superiors will make it for me and throw me out of here. I am heartily bored with everything, and in particular with the environment surrounding me. I master myself, I master myself moment by moment, but at times it seems that I no longer have a single spontaneous thought, or that there is not a single thing that I do without a sense of disgust. I drive my soul to a thousand acts of resignation, but I must wage war on myself with all my strength, and it takes an act of the will to drive off every contrary thought and persevere with my promise. Temptations besiege me with terrifying aggression and vigour, not so much against chastity as against the faith, or, more exactly, against every certainty. My soul is left stunned and dazed.'

As usual, Andrea had searched in vain inside himself for words which might relieve his brother's moral distress, a distress which was also his own but which he would never confess to other people. The only words he managed to find served to confirm his own impotence and torment.

'Why,' he wondered aloud, looking Brother Zanna straight in the eye, 'why do we not wish to die for what we love? Why, miserable hypocrites that we are, do we hate everything that brings with it suffering, and then preach that salvation is in pain? Why do we whimper like cowards, telling ourselves that death at our age is too hard?'

'Brother,' replied his companion, 'let's get out of here, let's go away together. Let's find the courage to do it. I don't know where I could go: I have no refuge, no house, no work. It doesn't matter. Let's face up to the future. We'll feel stronger together, we'll have a clearer grasp of things, a wider moral sensibility, a more healthy and vigorous sense of life. The conquest of a more spiritual human reality at the expense of the right to be fully alive is harmful, it's an illusion.'

For a moment, Andrea was on the point of embracing him, but he managed to control himself and, shaking his head, said, 'Oh, no, no, our real suffering should be in not knowing how to love, and our only sadness, the sadness of not being saints . . .'

That day, after these words, Brother Zanna had turned brusquely away from him.

Andrea knew it was only a matter of time before Brother Zanna left the novitiate. His lack of inhibition and his vivacity of character were scarcely suited to someone who aspired to wear the Jesuit's robes. He lacked that kind of insensitivity which had gradually drained Andrea of any bitterness over even the most dangerous offences. After the death of Brother Lodovici, the young man seemed to withdraw from all active participation in the world of human passions, as though the mainspring, the source and essence of hatred and friendship, of gratitude and vengeance, had been shattered inside him. Andrea hated no one except himself, and for him a return to the world would have meant affording himself further credit, or giving proof of a confidence in his own resources which he felt he no longer possessed. Nothing deceived him so much as that reputation he had acquired for himself of being able to deceive anyone. The deeper the disgust he felt for the outward forms to which he was obliged to submit, the greater his attachment to them. Such was his literal, precise, even servile observance of these forms, even of the most trivial of them, that every other consideration disappeared from sight.

Brother Zanna could no longer fail to consider him a worse hypocrite than the others and to hold him in contempt, even if he did feel that he had, cunningly, won him to his side. Although both had arrived at the same conclusions, they had nevertheless chosen different paths. Andrea, by shying away from the search and denying any further craving for liberty, and although still bereft of true faith, was making an effort to retrace his steps, to find refuge in mental reservations and in a false consciousness whose purpose was to cloak mendacity and avoid the truth. Brother Zanna was certain that Andrea would never follow him out of the novitiate, but would, on the contrary, remain as one of the range of types the Society continued to offer the world: the kindly, the treacherous, the ridiculous, the astute, the intriguer, the learned or the saintly. Perhaps he would one day provide in himself the most faithful of images of the perfect Jesuit.

Brother Zanna noted continual changes in him: he had lost that relaxed joyfulness of manner which he had once displayed. Now he exhibited an extreme gravitas which attracted the praises of the superiors, who asserted that excessive fickleness was an obstacle to sovereign dignity. Andrea made a great show of words which appeared to be taken from books and aroused murmurs of deferential agreement all around him. For instance, he would say, 'What is lacking today is patience. This endless rush has corrupted the world. It is essential to cultivate a redeeming patience.'

It seemed that his spirit had definitively accepted life in a rarefied environment which might at any moment suffocate him, renouncing, for the sake of fidelity to forms invented by man himself, that liberty which Brother Zanna, in his innermost being, craved so powerfully. Zanna considered tawdry precisely those things to which Andrea clung most tenaciously, the things which the superiors called virtues but which were, in Brother Zanna's eyes, anything but. He noted, for example, that Andrea no longer allowed himself to cross his legs when he sat down, as he had done at an earlier stage, in keeping with a tacit understanding between them intended to transform this act into a gesture of insouciance, challenge and protest against the facile bigotry of the other novices. On the contrary, Andrea now seemed to take delight in the commonplace, the hum-drum and the day-to-day. Brother Zanna, for his part, could not understand that, by so doing, the other had discovered a means of transforming the very perfection of routine into the exceptional. There was more than one way of escaping from the mediocre and appearing exceptional: not by rebelling, as did Brother Zanna, against the constraints of the rules, but on the contrary by an exaggerated observance of them, with a scrupulousness which in itself differentiated Andrea from the others and made him an almost exemplary archetype of the religious life.

He took comfort in this constant and unmoving fidelity to the most rigid aspects of tradition, which was also, to his surprise, an emancipation from the present and from the dull anxiety aroused in him by the slow passing of time, where each day was indistinguishable from the day before and each hour was occupied by identical exercises, physical or spiritual. In the collective rhythm of that monotonous existence, he preserved a certain infallibility, which, even if it did dehumanize him, pacified and petrified him little by little. He reached the point where he paid for any sin of individualism with a sense of uncertainty, discomfort, loss and doubt. Even if at times being behind the broad, collective mask gave him the impression of acting like a robot, Andrea understood that the illusion of perfect sanctity always ended up assuming the face of perfect sanctity.

In addition, he had been affected by the contagion of that subtle, ineffable, special madness at large in the novitiate, whose spread was facilitated by common interests and condemnations, by personalities who attained dominance through rank or natural superiority, and by a social circle that was closed from, or had limited communication with, the outside world.

Andrea had understood that for a real Jesuit there could be no greater mastery than the mastery of the self and the passions. It was here that free will, the semi-Pelagianism of the Society, was triumphant. Jesuits seemed to overlook what was most unyielding and terrifying in the human condition, that is, the irremediable. In a certain sense, they were closer to the ancients, from the early Greeks to the Roman Stoics, than had been all the anti-Pelagians of this world from Ezekiel to Augustine, from Calvin to Jansen. Within the limits assigned to him by Fate, ancient man preserved a certain liberty; he was able to take a stand against the Moirai. It had taken the heroes of the Reformation to throw conscience as a sop to fatality; it was they who had placed the tragedy of the irremediable inside man's nature. They had been unyielding and pitiless heroes. If there was no possibility of divine compassion when confronted with the inevitability of corruption, why should there be any human compassion either?

Jesuit asceticism had always been a protest against every scream of despair. The whole atrocious apparatus of determinism, which clung like a malign growth to the doctrine of grace, seemed to be beyond the ken of the Society. In the Society, the fact of human will was the most important element of them all. Everything was supposed to be unleashed by the will: the essential detachment from creatures and the indifference to everything other than the triumph of the Church Militant or of the Order. No Jesuit could be permitted to entertain any trace of contempt for good works: they had a relationship with time and presupposed the belief that salvation was an event situated in the future, to be obtained by the dedicated labour of the apostolate. The merit of good works lay in the belief that divine activity could, more or less, unfold in time.

Nor were they permitted to detach themselves from the world, to hold it in contempt or to take refuge in a monastic solitude which was a quest for self or open rebellion. The method proposed to vanquish the world was to imitate it and copy its ways, which were power, order and authority. This explained the rigour of the disciplinary structure of the Society, in which authority held undisputed sway over individual liberty. The result was that liberty was entirely sacrificed, so much so that men like Brother Zanna was never able to acclimatize themselves to the atmosphere of the Order.

Fundamentally, between him and Andrea, it was Zanna who suffered from genuine mysticism. Brother Zanna was engaged in a quest for the profound meaning of life and for some transmutation of reality. He felt himself to be at odds with the world and refused to make peace with it. He could not surrender himself to its limitations. In the Society, there was no inner tension, none of the innovation or ethical impulse which Brother Zanna expected to find around him. He was on the point of going back to the world with his dreams intact and unrealized, his yearning for freedom still a mixture of purity, incessant dissatisfaction and continual tension. In the religious life, as it had been proposed to him by the Jesuits, he had recognized the age-old stigmas of egoism, pride and violence together with an infinity of other natural virtues, which, however valuable in themselves, had nothing to do with those virtues preached by Jesus.

For all that, Brother Zanna held fast to his faith in Christ, while Andrea, some days, was convinced he no longer believed in anything other than that mound of formalities which he delighted in executing so punctiliously. Some mornings, during mass, as the moment for daily communion drew close, he could not fail to wonder if the little white host he was about to receive did indeed contain the body of Jesus. He was racked by secret torments; it appeared absurd to him that Christ, who was truth and love, had left his Bride clinging so long to an error as terrible as that of adoring a piece of bread instead of Him. Then he became conscious of his own vileness and compared himself to Brother Zanna. Zanna appeared to him full of strength, ardour, profundity, loyalty, frankness and a logic which yielded to nothing, which did not draw back from anything at all. He was indeed a soldier of Christ; with his profound sense of abjection and of sin, he was a passionate religious spirit. And none the less, it was he who would abandon the Society, while Andrea would remain, singled out by all as a model of perfection . . .

Unlike Brother Zanna, he had by now learned to avoid uncompromising statements, even when he was confident of his own opinion. He had been driven to adopt this position partly out of prudence and partly out that eternal ambiguity he acknowledged in human affairs and which Brother Zanna declined to recognize. In the Society, he had gradually managed to familiarize himself with the whole tangled web of inconsequentialities, flattery, subterfuges, necessary lies, self-interested silences and insincere attestations of regard or regret. He had acquired the art of concealing the truth, of knowing when to speak and when to keep silence. One day perhaps, like the others, he would also learn how to insinuate and foster suspicions. There was no longer, within his mechanical and atomistic concept of faith, any space for that mystical impulse which was the foundation of every faith and which had provided him with support in the first months of the religious life. The central, eternal problem of good and evil, of guilt and constraint, of liberty and servitude, of God and man, no longer weighed on him. He pretended he believed in the full freedom of human nature, without which the justice and mercy of God would be meaningless terms, but in reality he believed he had never felt himself to be free; he felt as though some gigantic, dark force was driving him along a path that he was convinced was not of his choosing. Perhaps he was only a sinner who had fallen alive into the hands of God, or the puppet of some unavoidable necessity. For him, the words of instruction or warning in the Scriptures had a hollow ring. He obeyed very scrupulously all the regulations prescribed for the novitiate, but he asked himself what value obedience could have if, in doing good or doing evil, he was no more than an instrument in the hands of God, like the axe in the hands of the carpenter. What morality could there be for him in the Society, if it was not dependent on the consciousness of freedom?

Being unable to go beyond the point where human judgement had to stop and accept the equivalence, or rather the probability of the coexistence, of the yes and the no, Andrea had renounced every further quest, shunning the extreme tension of religious concepts and refusing to engage in a worthless struggle with words and metaphors which went beyond the range of what could be known and expressed. In addition, he had a horror of solitude in the world, and would have done anything not to fall back into it. The contact with other men linked in an organization, even if it did weaken him, also brought him comfort and the flattering prospect of a more favourable future when, from a post of responsibility and authority, he would be in a position to exercise power over others. Brother Zanna, unlike him, would never be a success, because he had no respect for the unknowableness at the heart of all things, or for the ambiguity of everything that exists. When he had abandoned the world in search of refuge in the Society of Jesus, Andrea had felt that he was driven by a desire for liberty and peace, an ancient ideal of life to which he had attempted to give a new content. He had failed, and then, aided by the very environment in which he moved, he had turned to the old worldly ideals of power, hypocrisy, authority and rank whose validity was recognized even in the Society, with its severe hierarchical construction and perfect symmetry, of which he was now a part. The words of St Paul which Brother Zanna repeated so often, 'You are called to liberty, do not again fall under the yoke of slavery,' these words, which so inflamed his colleague and which contained for him the essence of the doctrine of Christian liberty, had an ironic ring to Andrea's ears. The naivety of Brother Zanna filled him with silent, unspoken sarcasm. How could he continue to insist on his own ideas in a religious society which appeared to appreciate only the art of compromise and the double truth?

It seemed inconceivable to him that Brother Zanna could continue to have faith in Christianity in its literal sense. Such a Christianity had never existed. The expectation and tension aroused by the kingdom of Christ could no longer survive, except in a few souls in a state of mystical fanaticism. There was nothing left in place of that expectation other than the presence of the Church visible.

Since it was impossible to find an efficient instrument of detachment and liberation, it was better to accept the old reality and the old society, even at the price of feeling restricted, enclosed and dead. By now, Andrea was aware that religion was not such that it could by its mere presence permanently expel every other thing, or offer him freedom from all disorder, impediment or limitation. He had come to the conclusion that there seemed to be a certain lack of common sense in all the world's old, stale opinions. The only certainty was death, at the end of everything. This was the human condition, and no one could say if it was a prize or a punishment. Andrea had entered life, whatever life was, only on condition that he would one day leave it.

'I shall be leaving shortly,' Brother Zanna told him one morning when they were on their own, cleaning the toilets. 'No one knows this apart from the superiors and you.'

Andrea noticed that his brother's attitude was more relaxed now that he considered himself free of the shackles of the rule and of discipline.

Brother Zanna went on, 'A week ago, the rector called me to his room. The novice master was there too. He told me that the Society found itself obliged to expel me. He begged me not to breathe a word of my departure and of the reasons for it to anyone. In any case, none of the superiors spoke explicitly to me about the official reasons for my expulsion. The father rector asked me if I had anything to say. "Nothing," I replied. They offered me twenty thousand lire to help defray the inevitable expenses of the first days.'

'I'm sorry,' Andrea mumbled.

'Oh, if they had not got in first to throw me out, I would have left myself one day or another.'

'What are you going to do now, brother?' asked Andrea.

'I don't know. You know, I envy you because you appear to be so sure of yourself, so certain of the path which you have irrevocably chosen, in here. I don't see what kind of dialogue there can be between us any longer.'

'Why not?' said Andrea, without conviction.

'You have managed to choose resolutely and coldly, once and for all. I believe in my individual autonomy and in my freedom, and yet, more often than not, reason and freedom seem to me mere words. Perhaps there are not even people who lose or save themselves, perhaps it's just that the way we were born is the way we remain. Andrea, have you never thought of killing yourself?'

Andrea drew back a couple of steps. Brother Zanna was facing him, small and pale, with that gleam of feverish life in his eyes, leaning on the brush with which he had swept the cubicles. He did not realize that he was, for one moment only, making concessions to weakness and to the sincerity of earlier days as he replied, 'Every time that someone falls in love they think about it . . . but now, I have put these thoughts aside.'

'Don't you ever think any longer of the things that are really you?' said Brother Zanna.

'I think of Marco, sometimes, Marco Lodovici.'

There was a long pause, which gave Andrea time to calm his emotions.

'I still don't know,' said Brother Zanna, 'if I should admire or despise you. Because I've still not managed to work out if you are one of those people, enviable in their own way, who have attained that equilibrium between asceticism, mysticism and authority which people like me have searched for in vain.'

'People like you, brother,' said Andrea harshly, 'believe that authority in matters of moral discipline is useless.'

'I have no wish to separate myself from Christ. I hate everything that prevents me from uniting myself freely with Him. There is no science of God or of his existence. There is no possibility of any theology, there doesn't exist any order imposed on God by the nature of things.'

The renunciation of his own powers of judgement, the slow extinction of any spirit of criticism, had come to seem immoral and contradictory to a young man like Brother Zanna, brought up as he was on a pedagogical system whose aim had been to stimulate personal, autonomous initiative, first in the child and then in the adolescent. He had rebelled, keeping intact both his liveliness of spirit and freedom of outlook. Andrea, on the contrary, had gradually lost every trace of naturalness and had grown accustomed to checking even the tiniest external manifestation of his body or attitude. He was aware that a hundred eyes were continually observing him. Mutual spying for the good of the community, dictated by a sense of 'higher' charity towards one's neighbour, was recommended, put into practice and made a matter of conscience in the Society. In his 'exhortations', the novice master had repeatedly invited the novices to report everything on other members of the community, even 'how often they sneezed in the course of the one day'. It was severely prohibited to alert the other party, 'notwithstanding', as Brother Zanna once observed to Andrea, 'the opposing opinion on this subject expressed by Our Lord as reported in the Gospels, where He recommended lifting up a fallen brother several times before making a public denunciation of him'.

The superiors had reproached Brother Zanna for, among other things, his reluctance to advance or insinuate suspicions vis-à-vis the others. He had replied frankly, 'I have no greater love for traitors who are motivated by the love of virtue than I have for traitors who are motivated by the love of money.' This rash reply had definitively sealed his fate. In addition, to justify his refusal to open his conscience completely to the novice master except in confession, he had appealed to the code of canon law, which explicitly forbade religious superiors from compelling their subjects to give an account of their consciences outside the confessional. The reply offered by the novice master – that the Jesuits had been given a dispensation from observing that norm which was valid for all other Catholics – failed to convince Brother Zanna. How could something be lawful for some people, he wondered, when it was considered unlawful for everyone else? 'You do not seem to recognize,' he had told the novice master, 'the abuse of power involved in your demand to possess people's consciences away from the shadow of the confessional.'

The example of other religious Orders and other masters of the spiritual life, who had counselled openness both as regards one's own defects and those of others, did not help make him budge. That, reflected Brother Zanna, was not the same as those clandestine reports peremptorily required by the rule of St Ignatius (outside the superiors' rooms in Jesuit houses, a letterbox was always positioned where anyone could drop in a letter, even an anonymous letter). These reports seemed to engulf the postulant on his entry into the Society and followed him for the whole of his life, up to the grave. Nor was the obligation limited to real faults, but it included an audit of defects of character and imperfections of natural temperament. This perpetual inquisition imposed on them, continually urged of them (every six months the novices signed a statement in which they declared themselves 'content' that all their defects and shortcomings should be reported to the superior), promoted by all means and invariably warmly received, produced in the long run a servile propensity to fiction and hypocrisy. A method of this sort in a religious society ruled by an absolute government endowed with an authority descended from on high tended to make it easy for the Father General and the superiors to acquire an intimate knowledge of each of their subjects, and to give them the ability to manoeuvre them as they wished and to use them for their own ends. The advantage this conferred was enormous since, under the guise of greater evangelical perfection, it contained a system of servitude through which the superior was able to draw to himself and to fetter ever more tightly the blind instruments of his own will.

Brother Zanna knew that in other Orders, such as the Dominicans, the brothers were invited to reveal only the grave and real faults of their neighbour, not 'everything', as was the obligation imposed on Jesuits. Nor was there any point in making comparisons with public denunciations in newspapers, since in the Society everything had to take place in secret. It was forbidden to attempt to get to know or discover who had made the denunciation or raised the suspicion. This was a point of such importance to the institution that, to uphold it, they had been obliged to obtain from the Holy See a dispensation from the contrary provisions of canon law. To abandon it to keep pace with the times would have meant changing fundamentally the spirit of the institution.

Andrea wished to make one last attempt to divert Brother Zanna from his firm decision to leave the Society. He was convinced that if he bowed to obedience and to the spirit of the Order, if he made up for his shortcomings, if he promised to change opinion and attitude in the future, the superiors, in consideration of his intellectual worth if nothing else, would back down from the threat of expelling him. The novice master, to whom Andrea turned for advice (and in making clear to him his wish to intervene in favour of his brother, he had to confess that Brother Zanna had confided in him and had thus broken the rules yet again), had shown himself quite enthusiastic about the initiative, even if it did seem to him useless. Andrea was granted permission to be on his own in the garden for a quarter of an hour with Brother Zanna. He told him that the superiors were prepared to reconsider their decision to expel him from the Order if he declared himself prepared to change his ways in the future, to renounce his stubbornness of judgement and his extraordinary freedom of criticism and outlook.

However, Andrea became immediately aware of how difficult it was to have any discussion with Brother Zanna. The arguments he brought forward to persuade his brother to change direction were the most obvious, most superficial ones, not the deeper, more genuine reasons. Andrea was afraid of tackling these. He limited himself to begging Brother Zanna to open his heart to the superiors, to speak openly with them and not to reject the chance of one final, clear-the-air interview.

'What am I supposed to say to them?' replied Brother Zanna. 'That I lack the spirit of faith? It's not true. That I entertain doubts about the Order itself? This is true, but they'd attempt, with all the subtlety at their disposal, to persuade me that these are not real doubts but temptations or merely partial and subjective interpretations of mine. I know that in the Society we have to bow the head and obey, or else leave. So why should I continue with this vain, hypocritical skirmishing? Is it or is it not true that I cannot read or write a line without permission? That I am not even permitted to speak about subjects other than those laid down for me? That, after all, I should think only about certain topics and not others? Is it or is it not true that the slightest, most innocent criticism of the superiors, or of the principles and practices of the Society, is forbidden? And if ambition is a misdirected inclination and therefore vicious both in communities and in individuals, how can it be considered holy, good in itself, permissible, invariably useful to the development of the ideas and of the prosperity of the Society of Jesus? These are things I could not know when I entered the novitiate. It has taken me almost two years to become aware of this, and now I've had enough. I have never been found wanting in my essential duties. It was due to an act of will that I entered here and due to an act of will that I leave here, just as you, Andrea, will remain here due to an act of your will. If I were to carry on and accept this life, I would be doing violence to myself. And for what? To keep a promise made to men? That would be madness. To God, then? God is everywhere. And He is in me. I will not leave Him here, I will take Him with me. If He had really wanted me to remain in the Society, He would have given me the strength to submit to all those things to which I cannot submit because they are against my conscience. And my conscience is alive in the hands of God, who never does anything useless. Basically, my history is nothing but the history of a mistaken vocation. An error, one of the many errors I have committed and will probably carry on committing in this great bedlam which is life. An error committed in perfect sincerity, of which no one is guilty except me. The priests who examined my vocation, and who approved it, cannot have been deceived, nor should they be held responsible. Those good fathers immediately saw that I was sincere and it certainly did not enter their heads for one moment that sincerity can often be the wrong standard for measuring the ideals and the emotions of a man. I have committed all the great mistakes of my life in perfect sincerity. That's perhaps why I can't manage to feel guilty. Anyway, Andrea, these months have not been wasted. There has been a deepening of my understanding of the faith. If I have learned one thing, it is that the religion of Christ must be accepted exactly as it is, with its lights and shades, its terrors and beauties, its intrinsic incomprehensibility and its profound mystery. I return to the world further removed than ever from that bourgeois, intellectual Catholicism which makes the Gospels little more than a handful of moral maxims and the Divinity a purely rational being, or else a God entirely of the mind but never living, much less lived. I think that the *religio depopulata* prophesied by the ancient Vatican catalogues could be the new face of the Christianity of tomorrow, even if the Jesuits don't like it. I think that, even if the Jesuits are not too fond of talking about it, the fundamental, darkest and most terrifyingly modern dogma remains the dogma of original sin. According to the ancient definition, human beings have nothing else in the depth of their being except sin and lies . . . You know, Andrea, I find myself constantly following with my eyes all you young people with whom I have lived so long and whom I will leave in a few days. I have learned a lot from you. Beneath all the systems, all the artifices, all the superstructures, all the rules which the centuries have piled on top of you, nothing seems brighter, more indestructible, more similar to the best of this world than your human qualities, the most genuine essence of humanity. The longing for liberty, which is irrepressible, will survive in you in spite of all the trials and tribulations which face you. And in spite of everything, you still know how to give the best of yourselves. If only you knew how much it costs me to leave you like this! I would like to tell you, were it possible, that I am not leaving because I long for something in the world I believed I had left behind once and for all. The fault is mine. I have grown accustomed to thinking with my head. This is the one privilege left to me on this earth, and it comes from being human. I cannot, we cannot, surrender this too . . . Oh, Andrea, as time slips away and the moment for my departure grows closer, I feel myself overwhelmed by a growing anxiety. I am sorry to slip off in this way, quietly, as is the Society's way of doing things. I would have preferred to shake the other boys by the hand, at least once (during all this time it has been impossible for me even to as much as touch them, since that would be a violation of the rule), to speak to them from the bottom of my heart, as I have done with you, now . . .'

He fell silent and seemed to be waiting for Andrea to make some gesture, or at least give some sign, such as shaking his hand or embracing him. But Andrea did no more than ask him, while struggling to keep his voice firm, 'What plans do you have for the future?'

Brother Zanna stared hard at him for some time, then adopted an expression of indifference and made his voice sound light in the air. 'What will I do? The most exhilarating thing of all is that I have not the slightest idea. If I am not careful, I risk becoming a kind of ideological adventurer, the worst breed that can exist in this world.'

He burst out laughing, and Andrea's unfocused anxiety changed into impatience. He wanted only to get away from Brother Zanna as quickly as possible. In his eyes, Andrea now appeared more reserved and elusive than ever. In a low voice, he started giving him advice for the future, somewhat unctuously. He made an effort to adopt an expression appropriate to what he was saying.

'Oh, Andrea,' replied Brother Zanna, 'I will be wise, wise . . . I think I will carry with me for the rest of my life a little of the personality of these people who have remained distant and incomprehensible to me, forever hovering on the brink of truth.'

Andrea's eyes met Zanna's, staring deeply at him. 'Brother, you will have to go through difficult moments outside . . .'

'I know, Andrea. I'll attempt to rediscover the rhythms of

life, and I'll attempt always to maintain an area of silence inside myself and not let myself be absorbed by things. I'll always be the first to observe them. I should have learned by now that nothing aids the development of observation more than silence. When we grapple too much with something outside ourselves, it's a sign that we lack inner intensity. This is one of the evils of the Society.'

'Good luck!' Andrea interrupted him. 'The important thing is to lay a stone on the past and not think of it any longer. You, brother, have taken a courageous decision, as courageous as any decision. Now you must always look forward. There are things which God alone can account for.'

At that moment Andrea decided to move away from Brother Zanna. He turned his back on him quite suddenly, leaving the other to gaze after him as he moved off hurriedly along the holm oak avenue until he found himself in the solitude of the garden. He re-entered the house, and then even those deserted rooms that he passed through seemed to him to have outlived their usefulness.

II

In the first months after Brother Zanna's departure, Andrea often thought of his absent friend, but always with a touch of inner malice. He knew nothing more about him, none of the superiors made the slightest mention of him in his presence, and the other novices had quickly forgotten him. Andrea, on the contrary, would have liked to know something about his new life in the world. What had become of him? It would not have upset him to find out, one day, that Brother Zanna was a failure or a drifter. He felt the stings of jealousy when, on the other hand, he imagined him attaining success, finding a good job and settling down to bring up a family.

Eventually, Andrea too began to forget. The period of the novitiate was drawing to a close, and the solemn day when he would take his final vows, binding himself for ever to the religious life and to the Society, was approaching. He had even completed the final trial of the novitiate, the pilgrimage, the one test they all looked forward to with excitement and impatience on account of that element of not exclusively spiritual adventure that was part of it. In the grinding apprenticeship and unvarying rhythms of the religious life, the pilgrimage represented a moment of poetry and freedom in which everything was for once left to the caprice of that Providence to which these artless travellers were entrusting themselves blindly.

Normally, the destination, which had to be reached on foot, was a shrine or a holy city: Loreto, Assisi, Subiaco or Pompeii.

The novices set off in groups of three, stopping in towns along the way to beg a little refreshment for the day and a resting place for the night. Their passage through the various villages en route gave rise to escapades which could have come from *Don Quixote*. With courageous delight, they would descend on sullen, old parish houses where their youthful high spirits played havoc with the meagre pantries of the housekeepers. Some novices fell to their knees at the first sight of the shrine or the city, according to the customs of the knights of old, and at these times the traffic was obliged to draw up sharply in deference to the indiscreet fervour of those black-clad adolescents, immobile in the middle of the road.

Andrea set off for Subiaco in the company of two older novices, after receiving a thousand pieces of good advice and blessings from the superiors. 'Do not forget,' the novice master had warned them, 'that the purpose of these trials is to train the novice to convert every spiritual experience into the substance of true life.' The pilgrimage had been rich in unforeseen episodes, some sad, others happy. Andrea and his companions had hurried past sports stadiums and had heard the shouts of the crowds watching football matches. He had made every effort to imagine the game, that elementary magic whose instruments were a ball and some white lines drawn on green grass. Around the stadiums, he had met couples proceeding slowly and lovingly, hand in hand. And he had asked himself how long it was since anyone had taken him by the hand.

Near their destination, they found themselves in a quiet, secluded, somewhat gloomy landscape, whose dark green was flecked with yellowing, autumnal colours. Within sight of the Benedictine monastery, they sat down on the grass before undertaking the last stage of their pilgrimage.

They were tired; the sun was setting over the hills opposite, and over there Subiaco had a fairy-like sparkle as the glass of all its windows gave off a golden glow. Beneath them, the shadows of the valley were ash-grey.

'Brother,' one of the novices said to Andrea, 'tell us something about your plans for when, quite soon, as soon as we return, you take the final vows.'

Andrea had stretched out on the grass, eyes looking upwards. 'What can I tell you about the future?' he replied. 'At no point in our life can any of us ever know what our superiors will decide in a year, in a month, a day or an hour. Is this not stupendous? Do you not feel genuinely free this way? By the same token, it is easy to understand the reasons for this rule, which doesn't admit any exceptions. The present and the past, my brothers, remind us of eternity: the future is, among all things on earth, that which is least similar to eternity. Has it ever occurred to you that almost all vices are rooted in the future? If the object of gratitude is the past and the object of love is the present, fear, avarice, ambition and lust stare ahead.'

That day, the two novices thought that Andrea would become a great preacher.

When he returned to the novitiate, the young man had to complete a week of spiritual exercises in preparation for taking his vows. He remained isolated from the rest of the community in prayer and meditation. Only in the refectory, in the chapel or during the time of manual work did he see the other novices. He had the leisure to observe them undisturbed, and was struck by the expressions on those taciturn faces: it seemed that behind them there was no particular depth, but simply an emptiness, as behind many tragic masks. How many secret compartments there were, he reflected, in the intimacy of all those isolated machines! Each one carried inside himself an unexplored world which was born and died in silence.

He did not attempt any particular external mortification during that period of retreat. He had finally learned, as a good Jesuit, to give only formal and fictitious importance to corporal penance. This made an excellent impression on his superiors, since it demonstrated maturity, a profound sense of discretion and the virtue of prudence with which he was richly endowed.

He invariably appeared acutely aware of his environment, more aware in the depth of his being than his superiors could ever imagine. Certain days he compared the novices, himself as much as the others, to frail swifts with broken wings. He knew that he was neither more nor less whole than them, that he had the same resignation, but he also knew that he listened with, perhaps, lesser humility to the raucous melodies of his sins from previous times.

As during the first days of his religious life, he loved to spend periods of time kneeling in the quiet chapel, where the scents of incense and wax hung in the air. The other novices, when they came upon him, kept their distance, as though they feared to violate his retreat in preparation for the great event of the religious vows. Andrea felt them gathering around him and occasionally observing him, furtively. Their eyes sought him out, hungrily and questioningly, testifying their own restless curiosity. They seemed to carry a reproach: you have made it, you have managed to reach the harbour after two years of torments, of cruel trials, of disappointments, bitterness and distress . . . Lucky you! Who knows if we too will be able to make it! There's no point, come on!, in you assuming that contrite, serious, priest-like air . . . All you want to do is heave one deep sigh, give one huge shrug of the shoulders to pay them back for all you've had to go through . . .

Andrea felt their eyes, their questions and their invectives strike and sting him on the back of the neck. And if he turned round suddenly to return their stare, it seemed to him that those boys, who assumed once more the appearance of impassivity, had never known the extremes of emotion and had always contented themselves with that monotonous regime, those neutral feelings, those squalid pleasures permitted them in their meticulously calculated style of life. Once again, as it had done in his first days, this made a deep impression on him. What imposed itself on his vision was not so much their individual personalities as that force which derives from something as simple as a collective outlook.

The morning when the ceremony of the final vows was due to take place, the young man left the novitiate early, at sunrise, for a walk on his own round Lake Nemi. He had been given exceptional permission to go out without any other companion. He wished to be left alone a little to re-order his ideas.

He walked briskly, head bent. In the glimmering air and light of the thickly clustered evergreens, he felt a new season being announced for him. 'Lord, be at my side on my solitary journey.' No other words came to his lips. On the banks of the deep enclosed lake, birds' footprints were lightly traced on a clay so soft that the human foot sank into it, and thick elders were interwoven with graceful locust trees. When he emerged from the wood, which, with its mysterious recesses of foliage, seemed to grow thicker by the moment, Andrea caught sight, in the soft distance of tree and sky, of the huddled village on the far side of the lake. All around him rose up that mixture of sharp and soft scents given off by the earth's vapours in the strengthening sun. From the other side of the lake, on the Nemi road, the wind rose and blew against the traveller in great, refreshing gusts, each one carrying a fresh scent of flowing waters, of woods washed in the rain and of cleansed earth. The sun climbed slowly in the raw brightness of the sky.

Andrea reached a country church, and lingered in the cloistered peace of the overgrown churchyard. The wind whistled through the ferns like a furious river. The novice entered the deserted church: a nun knelt alone in front of the high altar. She turned round when she heard him enter. Andrea watched her fat, square face tremble in the half-light of the temple. He knelt down behind the nun. The red sanctuary lamp, the flickering, adoring sentinel of the tabernacle, was burning in front of the altar. 'Oh, Jesus,' said Andrea, 'Lord, of your goodness listen, listen to our words . . .' He heard the woman weeping nearby and then he felt himself overwhelmed by an imprecise sweetness. He found peace in the soft music of those female tears, futile and imperceptible as they were. The nun's short fat neck was bent forward like a withered dahlia. Her great heavy body was like a stone statue on a dirty pedestal, and the statue seemed both to hint at and offer itself for an invisible journey towards the kingdom and the glory.

On coming out of the church, he no longer found the clear, taut sky blown by dry winds of shortly before. The countryside was dark with tepid, driving rains. The water channels had overflown, and the lowered sewers held only stagnant water covered by a thick, weedy slime. Then, along the way, the rains stopped. Andrea met some poor people bent double under the weight of the bundles of twigs they had gone to gather in the woods. Under the yielding circuit of its high, wooded banks, Lake Nemi seemed like a Cyclops eye, vitreous and gloomy, blinking on to the world. In the rigid stillness of the air, the trees, wet with dew, stood over the immolated branches on the ground.

When the young man returned home, the rains started again. And for the whole of that day, a slow, windless rain continued to fall from horizon to horizon in a low, dull, sticky air. The cold penetrated the bones. The novitiate house was ancient and everything in there was mist, dripping damp, filth and ruin.

A few minutes before the ceremony of the final vows, which was scheduled for eleven o'clock, Andrea walked along to the novice master's room and told him he felt unworthy of donning Jesuit robes for ever.

The superior smiled and embraced him. 'These are holy scruples, my son . . . We have all experienced them. But grace has always been content to superimpose itself on nature, to correct it, give it some direction, without ever being able to destroy it. And nature can be beguiling and sweet, it can often offer us comforts, but it was created in sin and is almost always fiendish, malevolent and blind. We are all subject to the flesh.'

Andrea had drawn near to the window and was staring out. Down there, on the far side of the plain cut into little squares by the speeding shadows of the clouds, the waves of the sea had turned black.

'The Society is proud,' the novice master went on, 'to bind itself indissolubly to you, Andrea. You have overcome the difficult tests of the novitiate. In the future, you will be able to reap such an abundant harvest of merit as to be able to fly immediately to heaven after death.'

The novice looked his spiritual director in the face. 'Oh, reverend father, at times it seems that heaven is behind me, not ahead of me.'

'Heaven is in us, my son, if we do not allow it to turn arid . . .'

Andrea had to make an effort to persuade himself that the priest was not making fun of him, and of himself along with him, in some monstrous, corrupt game. He refused to believe that, in the world, creatures could exist exclusively for the evil they were able to do each other.

'We are all that there is . . .' he whispered, as though speaking to himself.

'What did you say?' said the priest, who had not understood.

'Nothing,' said Andrea, who carried on looking out of the window at the dark light on the hillsides, at the softness of the trees green with musk and woolly with lichen.

'And now you must hurry, my son. You have hardly time to put on the new robes,' said the novice master, all vigour, bustle and tension as he pushed Andrea out into the corridor.

The young man stood as straight as a pine tree in the centre of the chapel, facing the flower-strewn altar, while the whole community chanted in chorus for him. His eyes had the tints of black glass and there was a kind of dark energy in that lean body now dedicated to the religious life. He felt no emotion whatsoever, and it was right that a perfect Jesuit should remain unmoved even at such a moment. For months and months Andrea had looked forward to every act of that solemn yet simple ceremony, and now everything was unfolding mechanically under his uninterested eyes.

He thought of Zanna and of his decision to leave. For him, choosing had meant asserting his own freedom. He thought of Marco and lingered long over this thought. Of Marco, of that confident, beautiful world of his which he had blown apart, and it had been a terrible thing . . . If he was here now, standing immobile at the centre of this ceremony, even if feeling estranged from it, it was in part to be credited to, or blamed on, Marco. Marco had made the decision for him, and Andrea had never managed to dishonour the promise made to him on his deathbed. For that reason, he felt a touch of irritation when he thought of Marco. That dead man had kept him bound to himself more tightly than any living creature . . .

'No, no,' said Andrea to himself, 'I do believe he always wanted to do the right thing by me.'

Meantime, the chorus was singing of celestial things, of the glorious prospects for the faithful and of the wondrous seasons of the world up there.

'If I knew what I have done to deserve it, I could even accept it with serenity,' said Andrea softly.

The persistent memory of Marco seemed to carve out on his face a labyrinth of tiny wrinkles. And that face, which bore traces of relief and regret, attracted the gratified attention of the novice master, who praised the compunction and the grave, inner sensibility displayed by the novice at this solemn moment. When, by chance, Andrea caught the paternal eyes of the superior, his ardent, thoughtful face with its obstinate, tense expression seemed to dissolve into a tender but controlled smile.

After the ceremony and the lunch, there was a period of special recreation during which he took his leave of the community of novices. In the afternoon, he had to prepare his cases for his immediate transfer to Rome, where he would continue his spiritual education and begin his academic education by attending courses in philosophy and theology. That last night he did not sleep. Tossing and turning in his bed, he lay awaiting the dawn, a dawn of unbearable sadness.

After mass, he obtained permission for another solitary walk round Lake Nemi, to those spots he was on the point of leaving for ever. He quickly reached the dark waters of the lake, where the spray rose from the waves as they lapped, rippling, against the shore. He continued to think of Marco, as though leaving the district meant abandoning for ever the memory of his departed friend. And he realized that that persistent memory, from which he did not appear to be able to free himself, still held him in its emotional power.

Marco had once expressed the wish that he would see him happy, but not with a natural happiness. And now Andrea found himself constantly wondering, as he had when the brother was still alive, what he could have done to make him happy or to be of service to him. Then, with some dismay, he found himself thinking that Marco would never have been able to be happy with him, not even now that he had tied himself permanently to the religious life. Andrea had always been able to lie to everyone, even to himself, but not to Marco. Still, unflinchingly, as he had before the novice had died, he continued to desire to receive from him perhaps pain and suffering, even further disappointment, anything at all, but not abandonment. If there was no further trace of sensuality in him when he thought of Marco, why did he hold so fast to his desire to remember him, to forget himself totally hour after hour with his departed friend, far from the company of other people, in perfect, inner solitude? That memory would have faded in time without the secret nourishment which kept it alive.

Andrea persuaded himself that in reality Brother Lodovici had not succeeded in transforming him, not even now that he was dead. Marco had deluded himself that he had achieved a work of reform and moral direction on his brother, but Andrea had been stronger than him, and his human attachment had transcended the limits even of absence and death. In order to transform him, Marco would have had to achieve the miracle of disappearing completely from his mind and heart, of destroying totally the memory of himself which, on the contrary, lingered on in Andrea's mind, unaltered and with greater poignancy. Until he managed to obtain a complete renunciation of the image of himself that he had left behind, Marco would never truly win.

The novice master smiled when Andrea took his leave of him. 'My son,' he said, as he gave him his blessing, 'if the present seems hard to live through, and the past has been nothing but mortification and expiation, the future will glorify the spirit of renunciation which has animated you. Because you have indeed searched for what is good and your sacrifice will be the most enduring service you could have rendered to yourself.'

In the presence of the father rector, it was Andrea's turn to weep in silence. The superior of the house, unlike the novice master, had not given up his habitual expression of austere firmness. His needle-like gaze fixed on Andrea.

'What makes you weep, my son? These should be memorable days for you, days of legitimate satisfaction and holy pride. You have given proof of fidelity, you have been called to be part of the "celebrated society", to use the words of Bossuet.'

'His are pure tears,' interrupted the novice master, who was also present at the encounter.

'Oh, yes, undoubtedly,' said the rector, 'when they are the outcome of noble conflicts, tears are never useless, they can even be fruitful. Even in prayer, tears are an indispensable corollary. Excellent for the education of the young. But let us never forget that we are soldiers of the Society, front-line combatants for the Kingdom and the Church visible. In this unending struggle, tears are of value to a certain extent, but they are weapons to be used with extreme caution. It is of the utmost importance to avoid tainting our inner life with sentimentality, or imposing on it the rhythms of drama. The important thing is always to be strong and to know how to create the right circumstances for every occasion. Let us be on our guard against cutting too deeply into the very quick of our soul, even if we do have the apostolic intention of saving it. Our soul is the property of the Society, of the superiors who are its legitimate custodians, and the authorized interpreters of the divine will. It is they who, when the time is right, will seek to mould our souls. We, for our part, must concern ourselves with winning the souls of others to the faith and to the Church. We must begin to love souls precisely at the moment when they have learned to sin. We must have a terrible faith in souls and a terrible belief in human beings. If there is one really grave sin, it is the sin of the abandonment by us of souls.'

He fell silent. Little drops of sweat ran down his face to form into beads on his throat just above the starched collar. He blew his nose, furrowing his forehead as he did so. He coughed. Finally, he rose to his feet. 'Good, my son, I hope you will in the future show yourself worthy of the holy Society of St Ignatius. I perceive a kind of overpowering concern in you. And you have demonstrated manliness in distancing yourself from every unduly natural link with other creatures. We Jesuits have abandoned everything, even the family, for the sake of eternal salvation. Only one passion is permitted us, the passion which empowered the saints. Have you ever noted, my son, that the saints are the most passionate beings on this earth? Even the death of Our Lord was the supreme coronation of his sublime passion for the world and for humanity. Fundamentally, what our holy father Ignatius demands of us is that we never renounce suffering. Suffering is our best prayer and our true ransom. We are crucified to the world for the salvation of the world. To renounce suffering would mean to have no respect for human weakness. And now goodbye, my son. Tomorrow I will celebrate mass for your special intentions.'

Andrea set off alone at nightfall with his suitcase in his hand. He got on to the bus for Rome and spent the journey pursuing the wan fragments of his spent desires. A new home was waiting for him, new duties, new responsibilities and strange new faces. There was not even a friend's shadow near him. Perhaps there would never be friends in his life. It was up to him to find some means of living worthily. Why, holy God, did the art of living seem so difficult? Perhaps there was nothing more to it than possessing a touch of loving humility. Everyone at some point in life had a heroic, gilded period. Perhaps, who knows, perhaps it was just beginning for him. He had memory, strength and character. The superiors had considered him one of the best novices, if not the best. He would go far, one day . . . Who knows, perhaps as far as the seat of Father General, the black pope . . .

   He prepared apathetically to face all the little acts of the religious life, and with that resolution a broad, tragic apathy seemed to emanate from him. He would spend his life making himself whole, perfecting one fragment of himself at a time, attending not so much to the spiritual dimension as to the natural, human, formal dimension. In this unceasing labour, the spirit of emulation, ambition, his cold pride, all concealed as he had managed to keep them until now, would un-doubtedly support him.

He didn't know if he would continue to remember Marco, the only weak point remaining in him, to remember him with the vehemence of other times when, driven by the yearning to imagine him present, he would stand in front of the bathroom mirror in the novitiate house, pretending that his reflection was Marco, that he himself was standing there in front of him, staring back at him, replying to the unspoken, desperate questions he was putting to him. His heart beat strongly in his chest at those moments of wild rapture and his face seemed to be strangely flushed.

The arrival in Rome put an end to his imaginings. Walking towards the Gesù church, he reflected that he would have to put an end once and for all to those endless fantasies of his. Fantasizing was a dangerous symptom for a man dedicated to the religious life: it carried with it the danger of weakness of will and feebleness of soul. It was another thing he would have to mortify and master. Before entering the house, he decided to make a brief visit to the church. The evening service was underway and the baroque temple was swarming with people. Andrea went to hide himself among the faithful in the shadow of a nave.

In elbow-to-elbow contact with those who were praying, singing or talking, he understood as though in a revelation that his spirit of faith had grown frail to the point of disappearing. The designs of mercy and justice manifested by the redemption now seemed to him obscure. Would he ever succeed in being a rigorous, pure spirit, perhaps a little slow or reluctant to bend to the scholastic rules, but always willing to lend faith to divine revelation without hesitation, scruple or mental reservation? Would he ever manage to conceive of the Christian religion, free of all imprint left on it by the human spirit, as something which had descended from heaven to earth like a block of astral matter? Would he ever be able to overlook the relationship of this religion to the historical past of the human race, its power of progressive adaptation, as well as a certain flexibility which was bound up with it, whose limits could not be traced a priori but whose existence was beyond question? Oh, there was a vast, senseless, mystical vegetation surrounding the dry certainties of the ancient Gospels.

Once again, a deep tedium over existence seized hold of him, as did an awareness of the vanity of any efforts of his in the face of the vast flood of evil and wickedness. He saw all around him, among the crowd of the faithful, some exuberant young people, elegantly dressed and full of life. In them there was privilege, beauty and *douceur de vivre*, as well as independence of spirit, whereas in him, what a contrast . . .

He fell to his knees and raised his eyes to that crucifix which he believed he hated. No, he had no longer any wish to be afraid when he seemed to be driven and led by God along a path he did not recognize. The best he could do was believe: believe that it was impossible for him to see there and then, believe that he would see later. He must walk willingly towards that unknown where God himself was leading him. He had no right to hurl imprecations against the evils and imperfections permitted by God, to despair over his creatures. Even if their existence seemed to him a painful dream, he lacked the means to make a judgement. God was responsible, not him. His part was to familiarize himself with the thought of God, so as to struggle against the sadnesses which took possession of him, which depressed or excited him. He had no right to allow his soul to be swallowed by some human sensation; rather, he must safeguard it by going back to a simple, more loving, more substantial style of prayer. It was hard to realize that he was not yet dead to whatever attraction human, merely human, unrenewed, unspiritual, unresurrected life still held. His devotion had always been brief and intermittent: his faith weakly felt and almost continually ensnared by impressions of unreality. Everything seemed too beautiful to be true, or else things were going too badly for it to be true. He had never known the experience of groaning in the Holy Spirit, in the words of St Paul.

Perhaps there was no better prescription for the effective mortification of the passions and suffocation of doubts and anxieties than apostolic action. It led the soul to mortification through opportunities too numerous to be forgotten.

Andrea rose to his feet and went slowly out of the church towards the building next door.